The Pretty
Women of Paris

The Pretty Women of Paris

Their Names and Addresses,
Qualities and Faults,
being a Complete Directory or
Guide to Pleasure
for Visitors to the Gay City

WITH AN INTRODUCTION BY
ROBIN DE BEAUMONT

WORDSWORTH CLASSICS

Original edition privately printed 1883
at the press of the Prefecture de Police, Paris
by subscription of the members of
the principal Parisian clubs

This edition published 1996 by
Wordsworth Editions Limited
Cumberland House, Crib Street
Ware, Hertfordshire SG12 9ET

ISBN 1 85326 628 0

Typeset by Antony Gray
Printed and bound in Great Britain by
Mackays of Chatham plc, Chatham, Kent

Introduction

Directories of prostitutes or courtesans were certainly in circulation in England by the mid-eighteenth century, if not earlier, and one pamphlet of the 1750s notes sales of a Covent Garden directory as exceeding five thousand copies which, even if a wild exaggeration, indicates a certain popularity. These early directories were surprisingly similar to this present Parisian example in describing the physical attributes of the ladies in language little changed from the 1750s to the 1880s – and not vastly different from the present day, though there might now not be such emphasis on the condition of the teeth!

Various 'Ramblers' and 'Rangers' magazines containing the latest tips on the 'ladies of the town' had their vogue, though usually short, throughout the Regency. A Parisian equivalent was P. Cuisin's *Les Nymphes du Palais Royale: leurs moeurs, leurs expressions d'argot, leur élévation, retraite et décadence* of 1814 or 1815, which had reached a sixth edition by 1816 and which also appeared under the completely altered title of *La Volupté prise sur le fait, ou les Nuits de Paris: folie érotique, mêlée d'anecdotes et aventures galantes du Palais Royale*. None of these, however, is on a par as social history with *The Pretty Women of Paris*.

An indication of the scarcity of such Parisian directories can be gained by consulting Alfred Rose's *Register of Erotic Books*, New York, 1965, itself a compilation from a number of entries, including, among others, the British Library, the BM Private Case, Cambridge University, the Bodleian and Guildhall Libraries, all the Ashbee entries, the Bibliothèque Nationale Enfer collection and the Vatican. Even here there are only a handful of examples, the earliest being *Les Bordels de Paris, avec les noms, demueurs et prix. Plan salubre et patriotique soumis aux illustres des Etats Généraux pour en faire article de la Constitution* by MM. Dillon, Sartine, Lenoir, La Trolière & Co., dedicated to La Fédération, Year 2 of Liberty, 14 July 1779 (8vo, 24 pages, with a plan for a model brothel). In 1802, we have *Les Serails de Paris, ou vies et portraits des Dames Paris, Gourdan, Moutigni et autres appareilleuses, etc.* (3 vols, 12mo), reprinted in Brussels in 1885 and probably mostly fictitious. Another title with a Brussels imprint is *The Gentleman's Night Guide: The Gay Women of Paris and Brussels, or, Paris and Brussels after Dark* by 'Wideawake' (12mo, 58 pages), Paris – but Belgian printing – *c.* 1870.

But it is *The Pretty Women of Paris* which, by its comprehensiveness and obviously factual character, is of the greatest interest. The entry in Rose tells us that it was issued in twelve parts, 200 pages in all, each part dated 1883, but Rose's copy had no date on the main title page. The imprint 'Privately Printed at the Press of the Prefecture of the Police by subscription of the Members of the Principal Parisian Clubs' is obviously false. However, some clue as to the actual publisher might be indicated by the issue in 1884 of the final six pages with the addition of a printed wrapper and limitation leaf. Here the title on the wrapper is given as *The Pleasures of Paris: A Complete List of its Licensed Brothels or 'Maisons de Tolerance'. Now Published for the First Time* (in fact for the second time), and the imprint is Paris, Alphonse and Co., 69 Rue des Dechargeurs, 1884. The limitation, too, is worthy of record:

LIMITED TO 169 COPIES
(for private circulation only)
4 on Superfine syphilitic-green paper, for the use of
the Prefect of Police;
60 on parchment for private distribution among the
French and English Clergy;
4 on handmade Roger Mill for the Society of
Women and Children;
4 on rough vellum, St George and the Dragon
watermark, for Girton College;
100 on 500-curl-papers-for-sixpence quality, for the
private enjoyment of the common crowd of ordinary
English rakes, numbered 1 to 100.
No. ...

Apart from the apparent discrepancy in numbers and the obvious spoof in the description of the varying quality of the copies, the identification of Alphonse and Co. is probably correct, Rue des Deschargeurs being a small street in the 1er Arrondissement running between the Rue de Rivoli and Rue des Halles.

All copies of both publications must be scarce. The one from which the present reprint is taken turned up in a Provincial Booksellers Monthly Fair at the Russell Hotel, Bloomsbury, in October 1995. There was a copy in an American bookseller's catalogue in 1989 but there is no copy recorded in the British Library or National Union of Congress catalogues. Rose gives no locations but records it as No. 3451, with the six-page 1884 List of Brothels being No. 3450, located only in the Private Case in the British (Museum) Library. However, by the time Kearney issued *The Private Case. An Annotated Bibliography of the Private Case Erotica Collection in the British (Museum) Library* in 1981 this had been transferred in the large-scale post-1960s declassification and redistribution of material no longer deemed to be of such a nature as to warrant inclusion in this Private Case.

Directories have also been in circulation in this century. The *Blue Book* of New Orleans's red-light district made its first appearance in 1900, with a fifth and final edition in 1915, and listed a total of 774 women, made up of 425 white, 251 negro, 9 octroon and 72 white and 17 coloured cabaret entertainers. Rose's *Storyville, New Orleans*, page 146, says: 'The *Blue Book* . . . remains a fascinating and unique document. Each edition, printed by the tens of thousands and distributed free by barkeepers to favored customers or sold for a quarter by the newsboys who hawked the *Picayune* and *Item* at every tenderloin corner, is now a rare collector's item.'

As a result of the Street Offences Act, 1959, prostitutes were no longer permitted to solicit on the streets. In 1962 one Frederick Charles Shaw published a twenty-eight-page booklet entitled *The Ladies Directory*, most of which was taken up by the entries of the names and addresses of prostitutes, for which they were charged, together with their nude photographs, telephone numbers and services offered, including in some cases sexual perversions. Shaw pleaded not guilty at the Central Criminal Court on an indictment of three counts: 1. Conspiracy to corrupt public morals . . . with intent thereby to debauch and corrupt the morals as well as youth of divers other liege subjects of Our Lady The Queen and to raise and create in their minds inordinate and lustful desires; 2. Living on the earnings of prostitutes . . . ; 3. Publishing an obscene article, *The Ladies Directory*, contrary to section 30 of the Obscene Publications Act, 1959. Conviction by jury, upheld by the Court of Criminal Appeal and the House of Lords, was obtained on all three counts.

Where *The Pretty Women of Paris* differs from all these other directories is in the extraordinary richness of detail and insight into the period. It is as if a late-nineteenth-century photographer's flash bar has brilliantly lit up the Parisian underworld for us to wonder and marvel at. Courtesans like Lee d'Asco (her house full of all kinds of animals, her latest acquisition being a tame bear), who ascends in a balloon dressed as a man wearing a revolver, descending perfectly naked having thrown away her clothes to lighten the car . . . Or the 'mad' Mlle Lasseny, with a large barrel-organ behind her bed, in the adjoining room, who makes her maid turn the handle while she is enjoying her *grind* on the big couch. There are also illuminating little asides, such as the comment that poverty in Sweden is not so degrading as in Britain, paupers there being thought not as low as the women and children who tramp through Kent in the hop-picking season. Or the fact that 'the debauched girls of our manufacturing towns generally make their way to Paris where they find ready bidders for that which they are forced to bestow for nothing on their superiors in the country' (in this case in Lyons). Or de la Roche, for whom the *table d'hôte* of the Hôtel Splendide is a happy hunting-ground during the Exhibition year of 1878, who every year goes to London, putting up with a swell procuress and returning to Paris, as penniless as before, boasting of her astounding villa in St John's Wood.

It would seem that the author – authors, for how could one man have discovered so much? – must have been English, living in Paris. There is surely a reference to the future Edward VII on page 129 where, under Massin, he says: 'We have delayed going to press for some time in order to find the dwelling of this vivacious little actress . . . till starvation drove her into the arms of a lusty prince, who will one day be king of the greatest country in the world – the country that rules the sea . . . She created the part of Zola's heroine, Nana, and her life resembles greatly that of the imaginary courtesan.' Note also Mlle Melcy on page 131, the favoured whore of a member of the British Parliament, 'who also adores her own sex – but only when there is a debate in the House' (*plus ça change*) . . . It is gratifying, too, to see that the author is justly proud that Mlle Howard, the handsomest whore in Paris, was an Englishwoman who had been a flower girl outside a London theatre. As one might expect, there is throughout a strong lesbian undercurrent, Les Rieuses (the Merry Women) being a lesbian association entirely composed of Parisian actresses, formed by Leroux (page 116), which held monthly dinners from which men were excluded and after which they spent the night together.

Dumas, Offenbach, Sarah Bernhardt, the late, but not lamented, Duke of Brunswick, the silly Prince of Orange ('since dead after an orgy with Mlle Robert') – all make their appearances in these pages. Manet's *Bar au Folies Bergère* was a sensation in the Salon of 1882, Degas was at the height of his powers in depicting ballet dancers and Massenet was about to produce *Manon* at the Opéra Comique in January 1884. We are in the midst of *La Belle Epoque* – read on . . .

Robin de Beaumont

Contents

Author's Preface

Every woman has her price . . .

Publisher's note

In 1883, when this directory was first published, the approximate exchange rate was 25 francs to the pound sterling or six francs to the US dollar. For a rough conversion to modern prices the reader should multiply by fifty.

The Pretty Women of Paris

~ Jeanne Abadie ~

80 Boulevard de Clichy

A dashing, well-dressed person of about twenty-seven, who looks very well by gaslight, in spite of her false teeth. She came out at the age of fifteen, and being the daughter of the wardrobe keeper of a miserable little theatre in the north of Paris, was brought up in the wings, and became the prey of the 'walking gentlemen'. She has ruined many men, but in spite of that has never a penny, and is always being seized and sold up. She has tried to act, but has never succeeded. Her low tastes, arising from her early education, will amuse those whose palates are satiated with finely prepared dishes and meditate something rough and fiery for a change. Her tariff is moderate.

~ Ellen Andrée ~

Palais Royal Théâtre

A very pretty little fair woman, whose artistic talents are small, although her body is in splendid proportion for such a tiny creature. Her principal lovers are among the artists of the capital, to whom she has often stood as model. She has been photographed in many attitudes, but always destitute of all clothing, and these studies from life are to be bought all over Paris for a small sum. She is very simple and kind-hearted, but cannot write or read with facility, her education having been greatly neglected. She is about twenty-four years old.

Baroness d'Ange

RUE SAINT GEORGES

Nearly every visitor to Paris has noticed an elderly lady who drives in the fashionable promenades, handling the whip herself with consummate cleverness. She is always attired in the height of fashion and generally has at her side a young and comely companion. The old baroness herself is old and ugly, but her turnout is always a marvel of coaching display. Sometimes she disdains to drive, and a postilion, bewigged and bepowdered, with brilliant, old-fashioned costume, conducts this luxurious old bawd; while on other days a tiny tiger, dressed in the perfection of taste, dances up and down on the springboard behind her airy vehicle. In any other capital of Europe this person, known as the 'Shame of Paris', would be simply pelted with mud and stones, for everybody is aware of her trade. It is that which Martial, in his epigrams, so unmercifully condemns. She is nothing more than a *fellatrix*, or, to speak more plainly, she produces the venereal spasm by the contact of her mouth and the tickling of her tongue. Only a common whore provided by the police with a card compelling her to submit to the search of the speculum at stated times, she manages to avoid this disagreeable duty by clever bribery. Her house, which, contrary to the usual habit in Paris, is inhabited by her alone, is magnificently furnished and full of costly pictures, statues and works of art. The visitor is generally conducted to a splendid bedstead in the Algerian style, and after copious ablutions with rose-water, proffered in a silver basin, the goddess deigns to prove the power of that marvellous piece of mechanism – the female tongue. The snug retreat is also tenanted by two or three young nymphs, but none are so clever as this old woman. Her large fortune proves her vogue, as all Paris has passed her doors. Well worth a visit if only out of curiosity, especially as one short *séance* is only ten francs, with a slight gratuity to the waiting-maid, who, in return for your kindness, will show you over the house.

⚔ *Angèle* ⚔

137 Avenue Malakoff

A splendid creature, with bushy eyebrows, low classical forehead, commanding figure and magnificent bosom. She is an actress who has achieved some success in America, but her beauty doubtless made the public indulgent. She is very fond of her comrades on the stage, finding profit in the society of 'swells', and pleasure in the company of handsome tenors – such as the dapper Capoul, who accompanied her across the Atlantic, or the big-limbed Dupuis, the ladies' darling of the Variétés Théâtre.

⚔ *Blanche d'Arcourt* ⚔

11 Rue Miromenil

For beauty in stature and elegance in every limb, no handsomer woman will be found in Paris. She has a fine bust, and has just reached the ripe age of twenty-nine. She has a slight down on her upper lip, and affects a *pince-nez*, which gives her a very saucy appearance. She is very strong and a fine swimmer. Her lovers are to be found among the busy members of the Stock Exchange, and her only fault is the too frequent recurrence of some slight symptoms of venereal disease. She gives very pleasant balls and parties, where many young beginners may be picked up by the amateurs of female beauty. Last winter our brunette appeared at one of her *réunions* attired in nothing but a loose gauze chemise and red-satin boots, exactly as if she was only a simple bawdy-house wench. Her bosom friend, Antoinette Duret, whom we notice further on, was attired, or rather, *not* attired, in the same way, and soon all the guests, male and female, followed suit. She is very good-hearted and does her best to please both old and young. The smallest contribution thankfully received.

⸺ *Léa d'Asco* ⸺

69b Rue Laugier

A charming creature, whose high-sounding name hides some very plebeian denomination. She is tall, not over stout, and very loosely built, with a well-shaped nose and an old-fashioned chin that advances in a provoking point. She is a fair actress, and has appeared with some success in *opéra-bouffe*. She was first heard of some few years back in connection with an imitation nobleman, who promised her four thousand pounds, which he, doubtless, would have given her, if he had not been cut short in his swindling career by the indiscreet hands of the police. This deception, trumpeted abroad in the newspapers, led many adorers to her shrine, and she succeeded in getting together a few rich customers. She is very vain, and very dirty in her habits. She has just returned from a tour in South America, and has brought back a little negro boy, whom she takes about with her to theatres, &c., as an advertisement. Her house is full of animals of all kinds, her latest acquisition being a tame bear. Always resolved to keep her name before the public, she fought, at rehearsal, her fellow actress Gélabert, of whom more anon. Kicked out of the Porte Saint Martin Théâtre for this outburst of temper, she was next heard of as accomplishing a balloon ascent, dressed as a man and wearing a revolver. Why that firearm, heaven only knows! She descended perfectly naked, having thrown away her clothes to lighten the car. Léa is very amusing and perfectly disposed to bend to all masculine whims, no matter how strange. She is very large in her demands, but generally finishes in taking whatever she can get, no matter how little.

⸺ *Bacri* ⸺

38 Rue Pierre Charron

Here is a lady with a dull yellowish complexion, a Jewish type of countenance and little fluffy whiskers. She is not pretty, and is not very young, having knocked about for some time, and seen some service in Cupid's regiment. Nevertheless, good soup is to be made in an old pot, which accounts for her possession of a neat little *bijou* residence all to herself. This is her delight and her pride, not forgetting her very handsomely appointed carriages and horses. She will give the slip to her lord and master if tempted with sufficiently liberal offers; and will be esteemed a treasure by those who like females descended from the tribe of Esau and Absalom, who are the two most hairy men in the Bible, just as Bacri is the woman in Paris who can boast of the best bush that ever grew below a moll's navel.

Bade

MENUS-PLEISIRS

There is no accounting for taste, so we jot down this lady, whom we recollect for some years at music-halls and at theatres, singing very agreeably, and always provided with wealthy lovers, despite the fact that she is as thin as a hurdle, with rough skin and insignificant countenance. She is pale, with light hair and blue eyes. Looks well when dressed as a man but undressed is like a wooden doll – very long, very hard, with a bust like a plank and an arse like a rabbit.

Laure Bailly

15 RUE DES PYRAMIDES

Quiet, handsome, fair and well made; such is the simple description of this courtesan, who is worthwhile making a note of, as she has only been out two years. Is generally to be seen in the company of those Belgian aristocrats who sneak away from Brussels, where they are too well known, and run down to Paris for a day or two, for change of – hem! – scene.

～ *Marguerite Baretti* ～

46 RUE DU FAUBOURG POISSONNIÈRE

You can see nothing but her big black eyes at first, and when accustomed to their lustre, you find yourself looking at a tall, dark, elegant young woman, with smiling mouth, handsome nose and a dainty chin with a tiny dimple. Add to this a really good figure and a fine head of hair, and you will be charmed with the whole aspect. Her principal lover is a young banker, who is too sensible to be jealous. She is also an actress of third-class fame, and has appeared at the Variétés. Her sleeping apartment of white and pink, Louis XV in style, is easily approached with the usual golden key, when she will introduce you to her little sister, a few years younger than herself and shorter in stature but of the same Eastern beauty. The chattering of the sisters forms a pleasant duet, and if the amateur has a *good voice*, he had better join in at once, when a most enchanting *trio* may be performed.

～ *Henriette de Barras* ～

16 AVENUE MATIGNON

'Everybody for me, and myself for everybody.' Such is the incredible and audacious motto that this miniature beauty puts on her letter paper, emblazoned in a multitude of colours. We must not forget that she is one of the few high-class demireps who has enjoyed the advantage of a good education. She is a little lady, born in 1861, and she left her comfortable home at the age of seventeen with a young officer who deserted her after a few months. One of the daintiest little creatures in Paris, with a wasp-like waist that she contrives to make smaller still with tight lacing; a plump figure; small regular features and a most candid, innocent manner of speaking. She is very friendly with her female companions and likes to be petted and cuddled by any possessed of Sapphic tastes. She pretends to be descended from her namesake, the general famous in French history, but what does that matter to our reader, on carnal thoughts intent? Who cares whether she be of blue blood or of humble birth, so long as she be good-natured, healthy and lascivious? She is rather dear, being greatly in the fashion.

Juliette Baumaine

90 Rue du Faubourg Poissonnière

Daughter of a gentleman who earns a comfortable living by writing songs for the music-halls, she was educated for the stage. After graduating at small *cafés-concerts*, she migrated to Russia, where the tiny girl blossomed into the handsome woman she now is, about twenty-four years old. As neat and pretty as a little china figure, with an agreeable voice of the thin class that reminds one of the piping of a canary. Her legs and figure are very good, she having retained the smallness of features, waist and extremities proper to girlhood, while her bust has blossomed to glorious abundance. She is now engaged at the Variétés Théâtre, and not being often on the bill, has plenty of leisure time on her hands – *verb. sap.*

Jeanne Becker

49 Rue Caumartin

The Becker Théâtre is known in France at every country fair, its fame rivalling that of Richardson's famous booth. The old woman, Madame Becker, who takes the money, managed, somehow or other, to bring into the world a lively little fair-haired girl, who has blossomed into a tall, ruddy, impudent, healthy, handsome wench, with flaxen locks and saucy black eyes. She soon left the parental 'fit-up', and went on the real stage, where she attracted some attention in the *Cloches de Corneville*, especially from the white waistcoats and swallow-tails of the stalls, who quickly set her up as a first-class flaring priestess of the fickle god. She next tried the sawdust, and could be seen jumping through paper hoops at the Hippodrome. One or two nasty falls put her out of temper with the sports of the arena, and she returned to the friendly planks of the stage. She has quieted down, and lives with a young gentleman, who, however, is not always at home, so that all her admirers have a little chat with her in turn. She is a very kind woman, without an atom of deceit about her, and is not averse to letting her multitude of charms be freely admired. When not engaged in coaxing the drooping energies of her old friends, she occupies herself in the incredible task of writing dramas for her mamma's wonderful temple of Thespis.

Marie Beckmann

6 RUE LINCOLN

Marie's mother was a cook at Brussels. In that capital her daughter made her *début*. A local Don Juan met her one evening in the Galeries Saint Hubert, and for a supper, a new bonnet and twenty pounds' worth of old furniture, bought her right out – body and soul. This Belgian paradise vanished after three weeks, and she was forced to explain the mysteries of the Paphian groves at half a louis a head, so as to get something more than dry bread to eat. She then appeared in Paris, in the humble capacity of washer-up and scullery-maid in Bignon's famous restaurant. There she was remarked by an old debauchee, who had a strange longing for servants and poor women with dirty hands and soiled linen. He took her away, but soon left her, as she was too clean for his horrible tastes. She never despaired, but working hard, and being without mercy whenever she caught a real fool, was soon able to establish a magnificent apartment, with the help of a vile creature who furnishes prostitutes right out on 'spec', and gets his money how he can afterwards. His profits are two and three hundred per cent. She is very cunning but not over bright as to her intelligence, except when her interests are at stake, and then she is a demon. Marie is small in stature, not too fat; fair, ordinary features and her skin rather thick in texture. Her hair is dyed and her age dangerously near the dreaded cape of thirty. She is to be seen at every fashionable resort, always escorted by some of our club-loungers – of striking exterior and noble birth but with unfurnished pockets. She wears the latest novelties from the dressmakers and looks like a real lady. Is supposed not to accept less than twenty-five louis for a night's entertainment, as she is now at the top of the tree having by dint of perseverance pushed her way to the front rank.

Marie Bergé

66 Rue de Bondy

Just come out, having selected the Palais Royal Théâtre so as to get herself known. She is exceedingly nice, *petite*, fair and, although born in 1861, looks like an innocent girl of sixteen. Should not be neglected, especially as she possesses a very charming pair of bubbies.

Berthe Béranger

14 Rue Sainte Anne

Yet another actress of the little bandbox theatre, the Palais Royal. She has played all over the provinces, notably at Bordeaux and at Nantes. A fair slight woman, of medium height, much addicted to the use of cosmetics. The bistre shade under her bright eyes, sign of too earnest devotion to the sports of Venus, is always brought into great prominence, as if her mistress were proud of the two lascivious languishing circles. Berthe, called by her friends, Bébé, which sounds like the initials of her name, pronounced in the French way, is inordinately fond of lesbian love, and is always pleased to give herself up to the clinging kisses of her female friends. Like most of her kind, she is very greedy after money, and we may excuse her, as she has a little swarthy girl to bring up. The father was a South American, and she is well known among the Peruvians, Chilians and Bolivians who swarm in Paris. When not accompanied by one of these lusty, dark-visaged cavaliers, she is pleased to accept the homage of one or other of the actors of her theatre, and grants them, for nothing, what the descendants of Montezuma have to pay very dearly for. She has just ruined a young manufacturer of pumps and iron goods, showing that her pretty little teeth are sharp enough to gobble up everything. Should this siren tempt any visitor to Paris, let him be chary of his cheques. Her photograph is to be found all over the town, as, indeed, are those of most of the ladies who are dubbed actresses. We need scarcely say that the stage is merely the ante-chamber of their luxuriously furnished bedrooms.

Berthou

25 RUE CAUMARTIN

Another fair recruit of the Palais Royal Théâtre – an establishment that puts as many prostitutes into circulation as the London Gaiety. Indeed, this very charmer once appeared at the latter establishment, when her *troupe* came to the British capital two years since. It was there, she avers, that she got heartily poxed, but, to the honour of England, let us add that this is a simple falsehood. She was in the habit of going to any hotel, when sent for by rich visitors or when summoned by letter to those who had admired her beauty behind the footlights. One fatal day, the silly girl was called to the Grand Hotel, and there submitted to the lewd bumping of a used-up old Turk, with a limp and cankered concern. She soon saw that the Oriental debauchee had left lasting traces of his slimy passage, and the verdict of her lady friends was, 'Serve her right; why didn't she examine the article?' This is her only drawback, as she is only just over twenty, very pretty, with fine eyes and teeth, good figure and a profusion of chestnut hair. Her disposition is light and merry, so that she deserves support and encouragement, especially as a very little cash would be wanted, with a few sweets or some floral tribute.

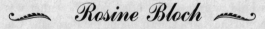

Rosine Bloch

21 BOULEVARD HAUSSMANN

In 1865, this handsome Jewish girl left the National Academy of Music (the Conservatoire) with flying colours, having gained every prize. She had no artistic ambition, but only tried to make her fortune. Being very beautiful, and of a calculating disposition, she quickly succeeded. She is tall, above the average height of women, very largely built, with beautiful almond eyes, rich crimson lips and queenly carriage. Although now about thirty-six years of age, she is still a marvellous morsel. She has retired from the stage to marry a rich Egyptian banker, with whom she lives. He is seemingly averse to conjugal bonds, for he ran away the other day to the land of Araby, and she had to go after him to bring him back. Rosine has a very nice-looking daughter, whom she calls her sister, so as to conceal her real age, although she has no occasion to do so. Under the name of 'Dangeville', her offspring appeared last year at a minor theatre, but was not successful, although resembling her mother, as far as beauty is concerned. Rosine has a *real* sister, Lucie by name, who is coming out just as we write these notes. She is pretty too but totally unlike her elder sister, just a head and shoulders shorter, and very much thinner. Rosine is a marble statue, both for the hardness of her form and the coldness of her disposition. Her pet vice is passive tribadism, and a pretty little Israelitish maiden, Lilia Herman, is often to be found *beneath her tent* or *on her knees*, *drinking* the *sweet consolation* that is *distilled* from the *altar* of female friendship.

Suzanne Boissy

We give no address to this lady, as she is now living at a hotel, previously to furnishing a new establishment. She can easily be found in Paris by enquiry at any of the principal music shops, as she is a most accomplished musician. This talent accounts for her long liaison with the Marquis de C—, who is the husband of that celebrated songstress who ran away with a tenor and possesses now a magnificent estate in Wales. He has another strange reason for occupying the position of principal lover – his beloved Suzanne is the living picture of his faithless spouse. She possesses the same miniature figure, small features and brilliant black eyes and hair. There is not a better woman in Paris, her kindness of disposition being proverbial, but she is too self-sufficient, and thinks herself the handsomest and cleverest female on the face of the globe. A real treat for those who like a little music.

~ *Alice Boni* ~

27 RUE DES MATHURINS

The very picture of a luscious whore. Large steel-blue eyes; thick, well-shaped lips; fair skin and auburn hair. Her figure is just what it should be, neither too much of this nor too little of that, and everything in its place. She has only just appeared upon the scene, having escaped from the clutches of the famous Mother Leroy, the world-famed procuress, erstwhile Rue Duphot. She got out of her debt by a miracle and now sacrifices to Priapus on her own account. She sticks at nothing, whatever *sticks at her*, so may be safely depended upon to wile away the tedium of a rainy afternoon. Please drop her a line in advance, and, if possible, let the letter be accompanied by a tasty peace-offering, as she is fond of pleasure, but fonder still of the ready rhino.

~ *Emma Bonnet* ~

1 RUE MILTON

This agreeable lady receives her adorers in a neat bedroom of blue satin, and before retiring to rest, strips naked and washes herself all over with perfumed water. She then strolls about her apartment in the same primitive way, takes a glass of weak brandy and water, and pops into bed. She is very industrious and when not acting or rehearsing at the Palais Royal Théâtre, where she is engaged as a kind of 'super', merely for the sake of her beauty, is generally to be heard of at one of the *maquerelles*, of which there are many in Paris. She is past the age of twenty, of medium height, with plenty of beautiful hair, which is now dyed the fashionable colour. She lost it all a couple of years ago, while trying to spite a faithless lover by setting fire to his beard. The wind blew the flame on to some lace curtains, and afterwards to her flowing locks which suffered severely. The sweet creature is pleased to accept a slight fee, and is not averse to a little pederastism – at least so say wicked rumours.

Lydie Borel

BOUFFES-PARISIENS THÉÂTRE

After you have seen this pretty blonde, who is young and fresh, acting at night, just put a letter in the post; and the next day you can either have her at your feet or kneel at her feet yourself – according to your taste.

Julia Borel

65 RUE DE PRONY

Julia knows how to take care of herself. She is on the right side of thirty, but her splendid figure and bright, piercing, fearless eyes are bound to command admiration. Her complexion is of a perfect white, and her hair is dyed to the tint of pale gold. She has made her fortune, and one of her chief sources of income is a bawdy-house in the busy city of Rouen. To an elderly gentleman she is grasping and avaricious; but a sturdy young fellow, and above all, a strong Englishman, who has never practised the enervating joys of masturbation when young, would simply be dismissed with a blessing, and have to pay no toll at all.

Zulma Bouffar

CHÂTELET THÉÂTRE

At the age of twelve she used to sing in the beer-houses of German watering-places, accompanied by her father, who was a Frenchman. When still very young, Offenbach heard her pretty voice at Ems, and after making her his mistress, brought her out on the stage, where she met with deserved success. She has performed at every theatre in Paris, and has granted her favours to all ranks and classes of society, noblemen, reporters, actors and theatrical managers. She has a little boy, and although over thirty, is still very tempting, as she possesses an everlasting fund of good humour. She is very stout and fair, with a large mouth and well-developed nose and chin. She is remarkably good-hearted, and has spent much money on those of her lovers who happened to take her fancy. The best parts about her are her posterior beauties, the Hottentot Venus not being able to boast of such a sculptural pair of marble buttocks.

Emilie Brache

10 Rue de Teheran

Of a crafty family of Jewish descent, this lively little kitten, who is young and pretty with a fresh complexion and compact figure, has inherited all the commercial instincts of her race. The whole of the family, which is numerous, has followed the trade of prostitution for many generations, in all its branches; dealing in human flesh and dabbling in auction sales; the trade of bad jewellery; negotiating rotten bills; pawning and other kindred chicanery. Her sister, Malvina, was once a great star in the world of pleasure, finishing up by disappearing into the curiosity and bric-à-brac trade, whither we need not follow her. Emilie hangs on to the prostitutes and kept-women who are well off, and tenders her advice with great success in matters financial. She is a fine judge of works of art, and after patiently submitting to the tastes of her customers, will offer for sale a bit of old china, or an 'old master'. Beware of her bargains.

Adeline Brémond

53 Boulevard Malesherbes

A very pretty little fair creature with a slight cast in one eye. She is about twenty-nine years old and dresses well. She was in very straightened circumstances a year or two ago and went to spend the winter at Nice, for the benefit of her health and purse. Her neighbour in the hotel was an Englishman, who passed a night with her and sent her a French 'fiver', which is worth four sovereigns. She replied, with a polite note, saying that she had duly received the gratuity *due to her maid*, and was awaiting her own little present. Since then she has been taken into keeping by a rich Russian gentleman, who gives her about four hundred pounds monthly, besides maintaining a princely retinue of servants, carriages, horses, &c.

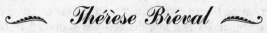

Thérèse Bréval

60 BOULEVARD MALESHERBES

One of our prettiest harlots, but what would be called in London 'a hot member'. Her splendid bust, large black eyes and pretty face have been in circulation since the age of fifteen, when her mother sold her in the Alsatian town, where the family lived. Her maiden-head was paid for several times, until it was impossible to deceive the purchasers any longer. Her father suffered imprisonment for robbery, and since then she has lived with her mother, who makes her work very hard. She is twenty-six now, and has never perfected her early education, not knowing how to read or write. She was a ballet-girl for a time, but soon grew tired of kicking up her legs for such small wages. So she gave herself up entirely to prostitution, and, thanks to mamma, prospered greatly. She has had as many mistresses as lovers, and a favourite after-supper diversion is the spectacle of Thérèse making love to one of her own sex. She cannot possibly sleep alone, and if by accident she should come home by herself, invites her maid to jump into bed with her. Sometimes passing the summer at Ostend, Mademoiselle Bréval is well known to the Belgian swells, who admire her Parisian toilettes greatly, she being always dressed in excellent taste. We must not forget a most interesting member of her family, namely, her brother. She keeps him; and he writes her letters, goes on her errands and receives her lovers, of whom there are always three or four ringing at her bell. He answers to the pet name of 'Lolo'. He wears fashionable toggery, silk socks, the jewellery of his sister's admirers, and pitches into her when she does not give him enough money. He is the darling of his mother's heart – a sweet spoiled child. Poor little Thérèse!

Jeanne Brindeau
GYMNASE THÉÂTRE

Sturdy brunettes, with large black eyes and a healthy body, are never to be despised. Of these is this actress, who really has great talent, her father having been a comedian of no mean order. She is only just turned twenty, and a few months ago was supposed to be a real virgin. The manager of her theatre, a greasy little Israelite, is reported to be the shatterer of her secret membrane. Whether that be true or not is a matter of very little import, as any admirer of this ardent beauty has only to apply to her vigilant mother. This matron is the faithful guardian of her daughter's charms, so much so that she answers all letters sent by Jeanne's numerous admirers. The burning *billets-doux* that the lovers receive, press to their lips, and carefully preserve, are invented and written by the cold-blooded mamma.

Irma de Bury
110B BOULEVARD MALESHERBES

Another golden-haired beauty, of diminutive stature but well built, with a tip-tilted nose and a silvery laugh. She is young and always jolly. A fugitive from the bosom of her family at an early age, she ran away to Switzerland with a handsome soldier, who soon deserted her. Returning to Paris she appeared in the nocturnal haunts and was snapped up by a gentleman who spent his fortune with her. When the cupboard was bare, Irma, sooner than leave her protector, tried to work for her living and went out as a bonnet-builder. But the ruined gallant came into some money and abandoned the would-be milliner. So she stifled the aching of as kind a heart as ever beat behind a woman's handsome left bubby, and fell into the general circulation, where her modest bearing and tasty toilette soon caused her to reap a golden harvest. She has just appeared on the stage, where she was a doleful failure. At home she is sure of success, and is always ready for an *encore*. At supper she is invaluable as she laughs all night, cracks jokes incessantly, drinks her share of champagne, never gets drunk, and is always ready to retire behind a curtain, where her white hand and agile fingers will be found very efficacious for those who enjoy scientific masturbation.

Gabrielle Calderon

22 Rue Bremontier

Tall and fair; grey eyes; big mouth and projecting teeth; with a fine figure, and marvellous waist. Two women lace her up as tight as she can bear it, and she does not even try to eat a mouthful when she has got her war-paint on. She is one of the few recruits of Cythera's army who comes of good family. Her husband is a successful novel-writer, but they do not live together, and he shuts his eyes to the free life that she has only led for the last five years. If she does not die rich, it will not be her fault, as she works very hard and intrigues as carefully as Bismarck. She has just bought a splendid private house, and has furnished it, too, without paying a penny for any purchases whatever. Everything is being done on credit, by an intricate system of bills of exchange which are to be paid, when they come due, with the help of Providence. She has several assiduous customers, and boasts that she feels a genuine spasm of enjoyment with every man that possesses her. Her age is about thirty and she is the mother of a very pretty girl.

Caro

Palais Royal Théâtre

Those who seek the animal in a woman, and care naught for brilliancy of conversation, will find a suitable article in this fine, dark woman with wondering, calf-like eyes and well-nourished frame. Her desires may be amply satisfied by the most meagre purse, and she is at the beck and call of all the *maquerelles* of the vicious city.

De Cassin

1 RUE DE TILSITT

Of all the sumptuous mansions surrounding the Arc de Triomphe, the one situated at the above address is the most handsome and spacious, occupying a square of ground that measures nearly two hundred yards. This palace is the abode of a lady who, although quite fifty years of age, yet shows vestiges of great beauty. She has played a great part in French politics, and it must be noted as a singular fact that she was nearly thirty years old before she began to be 'gay'. At that moment of her life she was simply a laundress, till a rich Englishman fell in love with her, and made her fortune. Napoleon III also became afflicted with a mad passion for her charms, and she profited by his blind desire to build up a colossal fortune. At the same time, she amused herself by ruining a wealthy master builder; and now she keeps the family of the man whose fortune she appropriated. She always liked to conspire and conduct underhand intrigues of all kinds. During the presidency of MacMahon, she was at the head of a gigantic plot to bring back the Buonapartists to France, and when the old Marshal fell, she put her house into the market and left the country. At that time of trouble nobody cared to invest so much money and she was obliged to keep her regal residence, to which she returned when she saw there was no longer any danger. Her diplomacy has reached from France to Spain, and once Don Carlos, a fugitive from his country, was hidden in a servant's room beneath her roof. She also fancied to become the mistress of a Russian officer attached to the Paris Embassy, and worming secrets out of him, offered them for sale to various governments, who, we are glad to say, refused her, one after the other. The continual state of fear in which this woman lives would be sad, if it was not so comic. She believes that her every movement is spied upon and reported, so she seldom goes out alone and never puts her foot in a theatre. Sometimes she is to be seen in the Bois de Boulogne in a closed carriage, but she soon returns home, where every lock has got secret springs. The door of her bedroom is bolted and has a large chain which she puts up at night, while at her bedside is a loaded revolver. She sleeps but a few hours each night, getting up at about four in the morning, when fresh sheets are placed on the bed and she goes through a long and elaborate process of dressing. When thoroughly arranged, painted and perfumed, she gets once more into bed and remains there till late in the day, to receive her visitors, who are dukes and lords. Her collections of pictures, lace and china are justly famous. In appearance, she realises the ideal of English beauty – oval face, with dimpled cheeks; blue languishing eye; fair hair, worn in smooth bands; and the reserved, ladylike, downcast glance of an engraving from an old keepsake. She is witty and clever, and has inspired great passions. The celebrated novelist, Alexander Dumas, was one of her victims. She was a long time before she would give way to his advances, and one day, just as he had got his hand beneath her laced petticoats, and was about effecting his purpose, she slipped from his grasp and rang the bell. The burly writer looked very silly as he stood with his person half-exposed and the maid, who had obeyed her mistress's summons, grinning at him. Madame asked for a glass of water, but Dumas, quickly recovering his presence of mind, exclaimed: 'Yes, my girl, a glass of water – *in a wash-hand basin*!

Juliette Caze

13 Rue de Naples

Of middling height, with firm rounded figure and bright, sparkling black eyes. She hails from the province of Catalonia, in the sunny land of Spain, but wears no dagger in her garter to protect her furry grotto. She appeared in the fashionable quarters of Paris but a few years ago, having hidden her beauty till then in the humble dwelling of a Brazilian student, on 't'other side of the water'. Her swarthy protector, having finished his studies, left her alone for a few months while he returned to his family. She soon got tired of this life of widowhood, and made a few stolen visits to the famous night-house, Peters'. When her gallant came back, he found that Juliette was tired of his *Brazilian nuts*, and had already become a shining light in the half-world. The little Catalonian beauty has led a merry life since then, with a decided weakness, like Chavaroff, for big soldiers. Her ardent, burning temperament leads her to select the dragoons, and a whole regiment would not frighten her. She dresses in the English style – stick-up collars, tailor-made jackets and a man's scarf and pin. She has a sneaking fondness for a glass of old brandy, and possesses a fine voice. Some kind friend has persuaded her to take singing lessons, and ere long we may look for her appearance on the operatic stage.

~ *Léona Cellié* ~

63B RUE DE BOULOGNE

Her original Christian name, Marie, was too common for her, so she changed it as above, and from a brunette became a blonde. She has a malicious face, not over pretty, but with sparkling eyes that have a deal of expression. About twenty-five summers have passed over the slight figure of this adorable healthy creature, now a fashionable whore, with more lovers than she can satisfy – even were she to indulge them in couples. She has, doubtless, forgotten the time when she used to live with only one happy male. In those days, the winter evenings would be passed on her protector's knee; one armchair sufficing for the two, the fireplace being so small. But she went on the stage, playing occasionally at small theatres, and the demoralising effects of green-room frequentation shortly mani-fested themselves and gave us one more common whore. For a wonder, Léona is witty, and not at all selfish; she will go out of her way to do her poorer comrades a favour. Rather weak-minded she is gifted with a lustful temperament, so that her passions often prove stronger than her mind, and lead her to try all kind of tricks and capers to prolong and intensify the pleasures of copulation. One good point about her is that she abhors the vices that formerly flourished in the island of Lesbos, although she has often aban-doned herself to the caresses of ladies not having the heart to refuse. But she justly remarks, 'It pleases them – poor things! – and does not hurt me.'

~~ Marthe Cerny ~~

21 RUE BERLIOZ

In the year 1858, Marthe came into the world at Rouen, where her mother and father worked hard at making copper saucepans. Trade grew bad, and papa emigrated with wife and daughter to Paris, where madame treated herself to a sturdy lover, who not only satisfied the old lady, but also tickled the girl, and debauched the head of the family by taking him out to supper, and giving him tastes for high-priced whores, champagne suppers and other expensive luxuries which are generally unknown in the ironmongering trade. But the false friend was soon found out, and the door shut in his face, while the adulterous wife died of galloping consumption, brought on by her insatiable desires. Marthe was then packed off to boarding-school, so as not to be in her father's way. The provincial beauty was soon taught the pleasures of tribadism in the silence of the dormitory, her school chum being no other than Thérèse Bréval, who not only taught her the mysteries of Minette, but also how to 'frisk' the fraternal till. Her father, disgusted at her growing vices, withdrew her from school, whereupon Thérèse became her evil genius, introducing her to all kinds of whores and bullies. Her hand was asked in marriage. She said 'yes', but pa said 'no', so she made another forced loan and departed from her home with Thérèse. The mother of the last-named sent the two girls to a procuress, who taught them their trade, and found them to be clever apprentices. Since then she has been up and down on the ladder of lust, and spends all her money on women, being passionately fond of those pleasures that she learnt at school. Marthe is a fine, tall woman, with long black tresses, large eyes, good teeth and a beautifully shaped bosom, albeit small withal. Being rather thin, she has been nicknamed 'L'Anguille' (the Eel) and were it not for her low tastes and neglect of her underclothing, would be still more in favour than she actually is. She has all the faults of a real 'red-hot' whore as she likes every excess, including the pleasures of the bottle. She has tried every road that leads to enjoyment, and everything that she has ever read of, heard of, or dreamt of, not excepting the tenderness of that faithful animal, the dog! Her bosom friend at this present moment, always to be heard of at the same address, is the nymph Marie Corman whom we notice on page 40.

Chalont

23 RUE FILLES DU CALVAIRE

Short and stout, neither fair nor dark, nice blue eyes, and, better than all – oh, my lusty brethren! – she is only just 'out', and is fresh, young and not of a grasping disposition. She sometimes acts at the Variétés Théâtre, but her talents are better appreciated when the candle is out. Then her erotic fury knows no bounds; she is here, there and everywhere; and, like a will o' the wisp, when the salacious amateur thinks he has caught her, and is about to press her lips to his, he finds that she has slipped his grasp and is far away beneath the coverlets at his feet!

Comtesse de Charbannes

46 RUE DELABORDE

Nero, say the old historians, was determined that every part of his body should be thoroughly defiled and prostituted. His example has been followed to the present day, but we doubt that he has ever had any more worthy disciple than the lady at present under notice. No mystery of debauch has any secrets for her; she is the true toy of the libertine, who, in his wildest dreams and nightmares of erotic novelties and salacious postures, has never pictured a more fitting partner. She is a short, stout, handsome woman and looks about thirty. Dark, with fine eyes, bold mouth and good figure, she is very well preserved; and, when dressed, and beneath the gas, scarcely seems more than about five and twenty. Many a lover has passed between her ivory thighs; princes and paupers have had their bellyful, but she goes on for ever. Money has melted in her shapely hands, and relentless seizures have so often been made of her various stocks of furniture that she has got quite learned in the chicanery of the laws relating to lodgers and landlords. In spite of her vast experience, she is still ready to listen to any well-dressed man, and her astonishing confidence in the honesty of the male sex causes her to be 'bilked' continually by unscrupulous rakes. She is a great friend of Antoinette Duret and they hunt together. Her title of Countess is simply fantastic.

Clotilde Charvet

23 RUE BOISSY D'ANGLAS

She has fled the footlights; and this fairy having earned her bubble reputation at the prompter's mouth, on the boards of the Palais Royal, now only seeks to please the brilliant votaries of fashion who give gold in exchange for erotic pleasure. Youth and beauty are to be found united here – fine liquid eyes, well-cut features, small waist and divine bust, which proudly advances its twin riches – such are the charms of Clotilde. Her hair, naturally black, is dyed a rich gold, offering a strange contrast, when in a state of nudity, to the other natural hirsute attractions of her fair form. She is a confirmed adorer of her own sex, and her agile pointed tongue has drawn down voluptuous torrents from nearly every actress who acted at the theatre where she earned her spurs in the battles of Venus. Be generous, randy reader, and ask her to treat thee as she would a woman of her fancy! O, ye gods!

Chassang

VAUDEVILLE THÉÂTRE

All the actresses of this temple of Thespis keep themselves very select, but the usual golden key will open the door of their nocturnal workshop, where the bed, the bidet and the syringe await the *coming* of the lord of creation. No amateur of facile female loveliness could desire more than she has to offer – a good, tall figure; fair locks; blue eyes; neat bust, that is naturally firm; and youth in the bargain. She does not use paint or powder, her healthy skin not requiring such artifices, and she is very aristocratic in her bearing. No one would take her for a mercenary beauty, so we may earnestly recommend her to those who like to show themselves in public with the lady of their desire nestling under their wing.

～ *Henriette Chavaroff* ～

28 AVENUE DES CHAMPS ELYSÉES

Petite, fair, with a solid set of teeth and a sweet figure, it is not surprising that such a bunch of charms was carried off when quite young from the obscure country village where her parents vegetated. A dapper commercial traveller was her seducer, and they lived together for some time in Paris – married, without the aid of church ceremony. A baby soon popped its innocent head into the vale of tears, delighting the heart of the bagman. But the angel died shortly after birth, and its father now abandoned the partner of his couch. Henriette did not grieve more than was necessary, but began to frequent the students' balls in the transpontine Latin quarter. She quickly became satiated with ill-paid prostitution and, by the advice of astute female companions, came over the water to the more aristocratic nocturnal establishments and frequented the Helder Restaurant. Her graceful chatter made her a welcome guest at all supper-parties, her continual gossip causing her to earn the ironical nickname of 'Bec de Lièvre' (Hare-lip). Doubtless her first lover taught her the professional maxim that 'Time is money', as, living near the Circus and the now defunct Mabille, she would often descend into the arena of illicit joys three or four times in one evening, never minding any *ornamental* or *fancy work*, however novel to her. One evening a Spaniard accompanied her home, and asked her point-blank if she could kill a fowl? Twenty-five louis were to be hers if she would undertake the massacre, while he looked on. The astonished courtesan accepted, and when the hidalgo called next day, a superb game-cock had been procured. Henriette, in her immaculate white dressing-gown, hair down, sleeves tucked up and glistening knife in hand, looked the very picture of a Druid priestess. She trembled not, but plunged the steel into the neck of the unsuspecting bird. A jet of blood gushed from the wound; the hidalgo looking on with lack-lustre gaze. At the sight of the cock dying in convulsions of agony, a lambent light shone in his eyes; his nostrils quivered; a strange cry of delight broke from his parched throat, and he gave unmistakable signs of venereal excitement, followed by the customary spasms of delight. The little piece of *foul play* was often repeated, until the noble maniac returned to the land of liquorice, leaving poor Henriette in the hands of the brokers. She extricated herself, however, by the aid of a gentleman who spent ten thousand pounds upon her and his racehorses. This stroke of fortune did not prevent her being sold up again, and since then she has been buffeted about by cruel fortune like a ship in a storm. She has always been fond of soldiers, doating on the military; although her passion for handsome men in uniform has not prevented her from also enjoying the intoxicating kisses of her female friends. She had just been seized again for the third time, and seeks to repair the breach in her shattered fortunes by that punctuality and strict attention to business which has always characterised the firm of Chavaroff and Co. (Unlimited).

Julia de Clery

16 Place du Hâvre

A mediocre actress of genteel comedy, from the Palais Royal and Vaudeville, but a good, kind creature, and handsome to boot. She is a dark, raven-black beauty, of the Juno type, with broad shoulders and majestic frontage. She is, perhaps, not very taking at first, but improves on acquaintance, being of a charming disposition, and always ready to laugh and show her fine set of teeth. She is an inveterate gambler, but very loving, and not having a particular affection for any one individual of the male sex, is generally disengaged.

∽ *Léonie de Cloménil* ∾

92 AVENUE MALAKOFF

We have much pleasure in presenting one of the queens of the Parisian whirlpool of pleasure, who merits her position by the stately character of her regal beauty. She is about twenty-seven; tall, with jet-black hair, which is entirely her own; blue eyes; delicate little features; brilliant complexion, innocent of paint and powder, and a most bewitching smile. The 'Beautiful Butcheress' is her nickname, she being the daughter of a well-known meat-seller of Bordeaux. Léonie soon grew tired of hearing the paternal 'Buy, buy, buy!' or its French equivalent, and started for Paris, where her *début* was not marked by showers of roses, nor did she walk in silk attire for a long time. At last a generous lover appeared upon the scene, and the honeymoon was spent at Nice. With the help of roulette, the love-sick swain was soon cleared out, but Léonie furnished a magnificent apartment near the Summer Circus. Here her fame began to get noised abroad, and with the aid of the foreign residents in Paris, she soon gained the high position she successfully maintains. The old English bawd, Cora Pearl, was her faithful friend, and it is believed that the two ladies were a little more than friendly. Nevertheless, Léonie has always liked the society of men, and of men with money, her lascivious temperament enabling her to withstand the most vigorous onslaughts. An Austrian prince took her to Vienna, and wore out his body and purse to please her, but all in vain, as she was found with her coachman, Adrien, a splendid fellow, whom she really adores. Some people say that he is her husband, and that the interesting couple are associated to pluck all the pigeons they can. Now came the turn of a great sugar refiner, and it was of him that she said: 'My little man has got several sugar mines!' Léonie is as stupid as she is beautiful, and fully believes that the sweet crystals that flavour her coffee are extracted from the bowels of the earth. She possesses some magnificent jewellery, and a fine collection of erotic photographs, engravings, statuettes, &c. She is very fond of her little daughter, whom she tried to foist on to the Austrian prince, although it is certain that the girl is the picture of Adrien. She dresses well, is fond of the excitement of play, and empties her bladder into a silver vase, her toilet service being entirely composed of that precious metal. A few months before the publication of these notes, she was burnt out of her splendid apartment, and afforded the neighbours the extraordinary sight of a real, live, French prince running to fetch the fire-engine, in his nightgown and slippers. She is very dear, but deserves a visit from all those who like to follow in the . . . *footsteps* of royalty and aristocracy. Alas! there are many such, and that is why expensive prostitutes flourish. How sweet it is to know what Prince So-and-So and the Duke of Thingummy say when they are just about pouring out their libation to Venus.

The False Cloménil

4 RUE DE ROME

Here is a sprightly young female, not nearly as pretty as the dashing whore we have just sketched, but bearing the same name. That is why she is called 'La Fausse Cloménil', to distinguish her from the real one. Her first appearance was made at the famous Bal Laborde, which is a market where faded flowers can be picked up at high prices, and now and then a fresh blossom, if the voluptuous amateur is only sharp enough. This imitation beauty is a neat little woman, with dark hair and eyes, and is very amusing when the bedroom door is locked. She used to be a great friend of Henriette Riel, the Dutch girl whose mother was strangled by a servant in the environs of Hyde Park, during the war between Prussia and France. She is also a great admirer of her own sex, and her tastes in that direction lead her to commit various eccentricities that prove very entertaining to all who seek to enjoy her strongly developed charms.

Marie Colombier

42 RUE DE MOSCOU

The restless activity of this little, dark, stout woman, who is now a few years beyond thirty, is something extraordinary. She has tried everything – acting, loving and writing. Her talents on the stage are remarkable; her cleverness in bed is undeniable; and her journalistic vigour is wonderful. She went to America with Sarah Bernhardt, but since the latter lady has got married, they are no longer friends. Marie is very fond of women, and during the journey would keep the famous tragedienne's feet warm and, by her luscious play, wile away the tedium of winter travel.

Marie Corman

Marthe Cerney (see page 33) is leading this pretty girl to the grave by the express route. Marie is dying of consumption; her vampire friend sucking her life-blood. She is small; well-made; and in her large, staring eyes burns the fire that is consuming her. She is a good creature, and is much appreciated by those who like a real, mad, delirious encounter; her consumptive state making her a very devil with the men.

Hélène Courtois

1 Rue de la Pépinière

The city of Lyons was the birthplace of this delicate, aristocratic blonde, who can boast of large, blue, astonished eyes; baby face, with microscopic nose; sensual mouth and pearly teeth; the whole surmounted by a forest of golden locks. She is well built; her bust is handsome – *pauca sed optima*; her arms and hands are perfect; while amateurs of small feet have nothing to complain of in that direction. Only about twenty-three, she knows how to dress in good taste, and is of a very loyal disposition, especially towards her lady friends – a fact which is rare among the demireps of all countries. She is often away in the south, having a large circle of admirers at Lyons and Marseilles. Courtois, for a wonder, does not like women, and has been really in love once in her life. But the object of her adoration, a dashing cavalry officer, broke her poor little heart by his neglect, and she now treats all men alike, as long as they are kind and liberal.

Marthe Dalbret

27 Rue de Naples

Her real name is Delisle, and she is a short, slim, auburn beauty of about twenty-five years of age. Her bosom is but slight, and her aversion to the actual act of enjoyment is something remarkable. Her centre of bliss is hot and dry, and as she is always straddling across her guitar-shaped basin, in its mahogany case, we may suppose that she has some great defect or hidden malady. But she makes up her ground by entire condescension to those of her admirers who care for pederastism, manual operations or labial pollution. In 1878, she was frequently visited by an Italian, who was madly in love with her, and very jealous. Marthe, fatigued to the utmost by the scenes of violence she was forced to undergo, told him one day that she had had quite enough of his fits of rage, and signified that she did not wish ever to see him again. He departed, vowing vengeance, and towards the end of September, appeared armed with some sulphuric acid and a loaded revolver. There was a fearful scene, which ended in the inexorable nymph of Venus receiving a bullet in her neck and two in her hands and feeling herself being bespattered with burning liquid. She fell, and the murderer, believing her to be dead, turned the pistol against himself and emptied the remaining barrels into his own foolish body. But death did not come soon enough, so he sprang out of the third-floor window, and died soon after his entrance to the hospital. Marthe was very little the worse for this attempt on her sweet existence, and the only traces are a few scars on her neck, which she is very proud of showing. A cheap illustrated paper produced a startling picture of the terrible occurrence, and Marthe bought a large quantity of the edition. To every lover she presents the journal, but as she works very hard, we may invite our readers to hurry if they want to have a copy – in which they will see their lady love weltering in her gore, and her idiot lover just on the point of jumping into eternity.

～ *Juliette Darcourt* ～
44 RUE DE PROVENCE

There is no nonsense about this actress of the Nouveantés Théâtre, as she is always ready to start a fresh *amour*, provided that the new admirer has a proper balance at his bankers. She is very tall, very fair and very pretty. Perhaps a trifle too thin for some tastes, she can boast of a sweet expression of countenance and a pretty little nose with quivering nostrils. Her blue eyes are bright and merry, and her age is not more than twenty-five. Blessed with a melodious voice, no one knows better than she how to give full, arch effect to a ditty of the smutty order. She is passionately fond of diamonds, and possesses a fine collection of the sparkling stones that will buy the virtue of the most virtuous woman in the world, when all other arguments have failed.

～ *Dareine* ～
14 RUE LABRUYÈRE

A stout queen of *opéra-bouffe* fame, with a fine, graceful figure and handsome face. She is dark and very lascivious, but easy-tempered, and may be termed a rollicking, merry whore. Like most stage beauties, she is passionately fond of actors, and is always ready to stretch her legs apart for copulation with any fine, big fellow who can exhibit a firm lump on the left side of his tights. To the outside world she is perfectly affable, provided the man who wants her is furnished with a crisp passport, signed by the cashier of a solvent bank; and truth compels us to add that she does all she can to deserve a substantial present.

Hortense Daubinesco

4 RUE CHALGRIN

Here you will find a neat, miniature, dark woman, who has changed herself into a blonde. Her teeth are good; her eyes are blue; and her bosom is small and hard. The little secret fortress is tight and fit for service, being well covered with a tangled mass of undergrowth. She is a bustling little devil, and has already been the cause of several duels, as she likes to be talked about and does all she can to keep her position in the front rank of the wanton trade by putting no price upon the pockets of the journalistic scum of Paris who, in return, give her many a lift in the scandalous chronicles of their printed sheets. From girlhood she has always played pranks with her own sex in bed, which accounts for her flight from home some six years ago, with a real high-born dame, whose reputation was a trifle damaged. They went to Vienna, and there Hortense began to follow the business by going with a German prince to Bucharest. He was poor, and after a short honeymoon left her in pawn at the hotel. She got assistance from Paris, whither she returned, and triumphantly ruined an old general, who is now dragging out a miserable existence in Havana. She now rolled on in a middling way, falling in love with a young officer, and ever after being only too glad to accommodate for nothing any mortal lucky enough to wear a breastplate or a sword. In May 1881, all Paris was alive with her adventure in the Bois de Boulogne. A dandy viscount had been her constant keeper for some months, having deserted for her a countess of the real fashionable world. One morning, Hortense, who is a fearless amazon, was enjoying her constitutional gallop, when she passed the lecherous gentlewoman, who was driving her pony and cart. 'There goes the whore who stole my lover!' exclaimed the countess, but the words were no sooner out of her mouth than Hortense turned upon her like a demon, and treated her to the prettiest thrashing that ever one woman gave another, never desisting till her riding-whip was broken into pieces. Like all women of her class she is a fearful liar, and her favourite falsehood is to say that she is 'hard up'. Ever since she began to trade on her own bottom, she has cried poverty, and now we hear that she is about to buy herself a little bit of freehold property, in the shape of a house and garden. Her brother is her valet and her mother is her maid, so woe betide the unlucky wight who falls into the clutches of this interesting family. From the foregoing sketch it will be seen that this queen of love has every vice of the girls of her stamp, including insatiable lesbianism. She goes the round of the nocturnal haunts to pick up some unfledged tit-bit for her private use, and sends flowers to any of her frail sisters whose charms she covets. Madame de Nolda, who also occupies her place in these pages, was wooed and won by her. Daubinesco dresses like an Englishwoman, and sports elegant patent-leather boots with flat heels. Never was a more cunning strumpet; never has a woman studied to better effect the passions of men. But there is no danger for a casual amateur, but he must be careful not to get 'spoony' and above all not to believe one single word she says.

Louise David

58 Rue Monceau

As cheap as a penny roll and just as common. She is a tall, fair, thin Jewess, about twenty-nine years of age, with a funny little pair of breasts, very low down, and just like two tobacco pouches, with no tobacco inside. She has no keeper or special lover, but lives on a rapid succession of short, promiscuous favours. She sleeps with anybody, for any wages, and does anything she is asked.

Lucie Davray

48 Rue Caumartin

During the Siege of Paris, in the winter of 1870, the streets were full of vegetable-sellers, and a bundle composed of one carrot, one onion and one turnip was worth at least five francs. A young girl, about thirteen, had plenty of clients, her beauty manifesting itself even through her rags. Her name was Marguerite Magnon, and she had come into the world at Bordeaux, in 1857. Her mother kept a fruit shop, having failed in the millinery trade in the south, and when the

Prussians surrounded the modern Sodom, the daughter transferred the business to the street. The National Guards of her neighbourhood got up a theatrical entertainment for the benefit of their wounded comrades, but, at the last moment, the heroine of the Roman tragedy they here announced to perform, fell ill. The little fruit-seller begged to be allowed to take her place, as she was longing to be an actress; and, learning her part in one night, she got through the play in a creditable manner, although she had been to the hairdresser, and her tresses were built up with feathers, flowers and pearl beads. She now calls herself Lucie Davray, and after a successful engagement at the Vaudeville, is now at the Palais Royal. She is tall, stately, dark and has a magnificent bust. Innumerable lovers follow in her train, and as she has no heart, and never gives way to the tender passion, she succeeds in amassing considerable wealth. One of her adorers abandoned a poor girl he had seduced, at her request. The forsaken one lay in wait for the faithless swain and shot at him with a revolver as he was leaving the abode of his new mistress. He was badly wounded, but recovered, and his fair murderess was tried and acquitted. Her name was Marie Bière, and she was a concert singer. The trial brought her into great notoriety, and she appeared in public, but always without success. A rich Roumanian offered her his hand and fortune and she has just got married to him. It is to be hoped she will be happy – thanks to a lucky pistol shot.

Jeanne Debay

3 RUE MEYERBEER

We place this painted doll on our list chiefly because she is a friend of the fashionable Reine Romani, who is catalogued further on. She was pretty once, as the shape of her features testifies, but now she hides her yellow skin under several coats of paint and liquid white, and her grey hairs are lost to sight thanks to the aid of golden dyes. She graduated in the whoring trade by following the unremunerative career of a provincial actress, and again in her old days took a fancy to appear once more upon the boards. She chose the Palais Royal Théâtre only recently, but Parisian audiences were too cruel for her and this pinchbeck dramatic queen has gone back to work in the half-light of her scented boudoir. Occasionally she flits away to Marseilles, having a large connection in that busy seaport.

Marguerite Debreux

NOUVEAUTÉS THÉÂTRE

Of medium height, with black eyes, bushy eyebrows and lovely mouth. Her cherry lips are always restless, and her sly tongue is everlastingly protruding in a provoking, lascivious manner. She is such a succulent darling and looks so well that it would be cruel to try and reckon her age. She appeared on the London stage, at the Lyceum Theatre, some years ago, with a French operatic company who played in English. She was very young then, so we refer anxious enquirers to the annals of the British stage. Being a strong, healthy brunette, with an abundance of black hair and a neat whisker on each carnation cheek, she wears exceptionally well, and although having just had a baby, is to be heartily recommended, as she understands the peculiar tastes of English rakes. When dressed as a boy, she looks a picture. Her figure, as regards the bust, is but slight; but her backside is remarkable for size and shape and we may declare without hesitation that she possesses one of the handsomest bums in Paris.

Clémence Decroze

4 RUE DE THANN

This is a very ordinary brunette, with a fleshy frame, who has a private house of her own and a select circle of well-to-do lovers. She has no more right to the name of 'Decroze' than the fair Laure of the following paragraph. But the latter beauty took the name first, and the similitude of their trademark is an eternal source of bitterness, as they are sometimes taken for sisters, etc. For the guidance of our readers, we boldly make the statement that Laure Decroze is by far the best business, and when you ask for that genuine article, see that you get it.

Laure Decroze

11 Rue de Rome

This tip-top siren was born on the 4th of January 1856 of Parisian parents who were in a prosperous way of business. She enjoyed a good education at a convent, and, when only thirteen, was taken away from the care of the nuns, being set to keep the boots at the shop of her married sister, who sells ready-made boots and shoes in the Faubourg Montmartre. Two years later she was the victim of a cowardly rape, but her stern mother disbelieved her story, and drove her from home, completely disowning her. She now sought the Quartier Latin, and went into housekeeping with a young student, who allowed her for pin-money and every other expense the munificent sum of two pounds weekly. With this modest stipend she was perfectly happy, as she adored her paramour, and often looks back with regret to those happy-go-lucky Bohemian days. The suckling saw-bones wanted to marry her, but his family stepped in and tempted her to renounce the love-sick youth for the sake of a bribe of eight hundred pounds. Money carried the day, and Laure was free. She profited by her liberty at once, and was taken into sumptuous keeping by one of the privileged, sworn brokers of the Bourse. He furnished her outright in splendid style, in the apartment that she now possesses, and where she has been domiciled eight years. Her petty Croesus taught her the value of money, and since then the careful wench has never had a day's pecuniary trouble. Her predominant feeling is the absolute love of gold, with the fixed idea that there is not a more miserable sight to be seen in this world than that of a poor, exhausted, old whore. So Madame Decroze, whose real name is Broye, always whines and complains of impecuniosity, thereby preventing the borrowing advances of her frail sisters in the clan of prostitution. Her fortune is already a tidy little one, and she means to retire from what with her is really 'business' at the age of thirty. At the same time as she keeps her eye on the main chance, she is perfectly docile and agreeable, and panders to all manly vices. When she lived with her stockbroker she enjoyed the company of another rich young lover, who spent six thousand pounds with her, and when he was ruined, Laure got rid of him, and he has just been kicked out of one of our clubs for cheating at cards. Our top-ladder lady is perfectly marble-hearted and feels no remorse, never having loved but once, she says, and the object of her affection was the student, whom she left for what was then to her a fortune! Her circle of customers is composed of the pick of the basket, no one being allowed to slip under her coverlet unless he can satisfy her demands for lucre. All she wheedles the men out of is transformed into substantial securities, and only the other day she sold off a lot of her jewellery in order to invest in the funds. She is of medium height, and her bearing is rather proud and haughty, as she evidently thinks a lot of herself, and above all admires her own astuteness. Her complexion is that of a wholesome, healthy blonde, with blue eyes, good teeth, nice lips and fair hair that falls to her waist. She is slim but well covered, with fine legs and glossy thighs, while her *mons Veneris* is protected by a splendid, soft, curly, chestnut bush. She is fond of walking exercise, and it is whispered that her pet vice is a curiosity to handle and kiss the secret charms of her own sex whenever she can get a pretty woman to submit to her embraces without hope of reward. She has never had any children, or made any attempts at abortion, so that if her heart is not in the right place, her womb is; she can present to her visitors a shapely body, clean within and clean without.

Anna Delamare

5 RUE DES SAUSSAIES

For a small amount of money, Anna will cheerfully give in return a large amount of pleasure. She is quite ready to please her customers, however peculiar their wants may be. She is fair, stout, and has blue eyes. Her figure is very good, and her conversation pleasing. She writes letters to members of the clubs, whenever she can get hold of any of their names, and urges them to visit her, pretending important business, an urgent communication, &c. The gentleman calls, and soon sees that the grave affair is merely the act of pleasure that is always so old and yet ever so new. Thus, the lively whore gains her object, and her daily bread as well. But she has more than one string to her bow, occupying her leisure moments with a little judicious proxenetism, so that if the visitor does not feel tempted by Anna's charms, she will not be offended but offer her services as guide and counsellor and find him plenty of little darlings among her friends.

Blanche Delaunay

ATHENÉE THÉÂTRE

All that we can learn about this brilliant beauty, fat and fair, is that she was formerly a servant in a transpontine bawdy-house. Her beauty soon found her many lovers, and, after a variety of changes in life, we find her at the theatre above-mentioned, where she plays small parts, such as silly servant girls, when her enormous bubbies are freely shown to the astonished spectators. Since her appearance on the stage she has got up in the world, and her tariff, from silver, as it used to be, now reaches to the golden standard. She became the heroine of innumerable orgies, and grew to be a ferocious lesbian. But some woman with whom she was madly in love, having behaved badly to her, she returned to the muscular arms of the male sex. At this present moment she fondly adores her dog, Azor, and makes no secret of her attachment to the faithful and patient animal. She has fits of childish sentimentality, and the other day, when supping in joyous company, refused to do the same as her female companions, who had gladly consented to strip naked and finish the meal in a state of nudity. She burst into tears, called upon her 'mamma', clasped her dog to her bosom and fainted away.

Delphine Delizy

19 AVENUE DE VILLIERS

There are certain small, dark, lightly-built women who carry their age wonderfully well, and remain younger in appearance than stouter females. Delphine is one of this everlasting sort. She is little, with mischievous dark eyes, and a slight, neat figure, with small breasts. Her age, at the time we write, is about thirty-eight, but we are in duty bound to state that she is still of very appetising aspect. We may call her one of the glories of the departed Empire, and the immense vogue she has enjoyed for the last fifteen or twenty years, may be explained by her wonderful resignation to all masculine caprices. There is nothing in the whole catalogue of Cupid's diversions that she has not done, or will not do. Her wicked, rosy mouth, with slight down on the upper lip, and hard-working tongue are justly celebrated in Paris. Her father was a workman and her mother, a camp-follower, who, when no longer able to sell her worn-out body to the soldiers, took to selling them bad brandy instead. At the age of fourteen, Delphine was sold by her respectable parents for the sum of six hundred pounds, and since then her lovers have been as numerous as the leaves on a tree. She has ruined several, being cruel, hard-hearted, cold and insatiable. One of her earliest lovers was a celebrated author, whose mysterious death some twelve years ago created a great sensation. He was found hanging by the neck to a sewer grating, and the secret of his demise is still a puzzle. Was it murder or suicide? He used to beat his sweet mistress unmercifully, but she has had revenge on the male sex ever since, as a small riding whip is one of the ornaments of her boudoir. Should any of her clients prove unruly or slow at unbuttoning their cash pockets, the little weapon comes into play at once. But some men like to be beaten, and find enjoyment in the strokes of a rod or whip, when wielded by a pretty woman with white arms. Delizy has always been pleased to accept the escort of mere youths, and she has generally four or five fluttering round her stiffly-starched petticoats. She sometimes amuses herself in extracting their pocket-money from them in small amounts, a few francs at a time, during the evening, under various pretexts. At midnight she turns them all out to make room for some rich, old admirer, and then counts up the tidy sum she has accumulated in such a short time, and all for nothing. She likes going out on the loose with a band of riotous young fellows, and her favourite amusement is to void her urine in the pianos that garnish the private rooms of the restaurants of Paris. Wonderful are the stories that are told of this clever, sharp-witted, heartless courtesan, who has had millions pass through her hands, but has never been able to save much money, as Nemesis has always been present, in the shape of some handsome, rapacious bully. One of her most magnificent keepers, up to within two years ago, was a millionaire who had made a fortune on the turf. While he lived she had a private house of her own, with a fine retinue of servants, carriages and horses, and every possible luxury. But at his death she sold everything off, and went to live in a small apartment. She has lately tried to get married, but her economies are not sufficiently large to enable her to buy a husband. So down the hill she is beginning to go, and is only to be recommended to individuals who are entirely worn out. Her conversation, barring a few choice oaths and obscene expressions, is highly interesting, as she has some spicy anecdote to tell about every notable moll or man about town for the last fifteen years. She rarely wears a low-necked dress without a ruffle round her throat, as that part of her otherwise handsome body is decorated with the scars of a malady which was formerly supposed to be curable by the touch of a royal hand.

Elina Denizane

13 Rue Miromenil

A new addition to the sisterhood within the last three years, and coming of a very good family. She is an inveterate gambler, and during her yearly visit to the baths of Luchon takes the bank at the public *baccarat* table against all comers. As jolly when in company as the proverbial sand-boy, she falls into fits of deep melancholy when alone, and for that reason is always giving dinner parties, and surrounding herself with friends, so as to keep her spirits up. The cause of this singular humour may perhaps be ascribed to a malady from which she suffers. The menstrual derangement, common to the sex, only manifests itself in her case once in seven months. She is known by the nickname of 'Fleur-de-Bidet', which may be translated as 'Bidet-Blossom', because she is always astride that useful article of furniture, which plays such an important part in the toilette of a Frenchwoman. No one would guess from the appearance of this handsome, stout girl of twenty-three years of age that she does not have the flowers like other women. Her fine complexion, dark-brown eyes and white teeth make a charming picture, and when she is on horseback she looks at her best. She is a good, quiet creature, and is a great friend of Cora Pearl, who is also mentioned in this list.

~ *Julia Depoix* ~
VAUDEVILLE THÉÂTRE

This diminutive actress has only just entered the lists, and may be described as a most engaging piece of goods. She is no taller than a good-sized walking-stick, but she has black hair that falls to her feet, sweet features, cunning little beady black eyes and a Roman nose. She has just passed through a trying ordeal, as her principal lover, the scapegrace son of a Jewish banker, on whom she doted, has succeeded in disentangling himself from her toils, and has made peace with his family by getting married. Julia was always very jealous and once stabbed him in the arm with a dagger that was not a theatrical 'property'. The wound was a mere scratch, but he no longer *draws his weapon* for his loving mistress, who is sorely grieved by his abandonment of her. The wanton minx always had a mania for getting spoony on poor young fellows, so perhaps this lesson will cure her and lead her to welcome the arrival of a clean, wealthy old gentleman with lots of money and no dangerous, dirty fancies.

~ *Clara Dermigny* ~
4 RUE LINCOLN

She dubs herself Countess and sports a coronet on her brougham, notepaper and hair-brushes and was very nearly having the aristocratic emblem reproduced in the bottom of her *vase de nuit* but was dissuaded by sensible friends. She is not of noble birth, however, and was well-known for years to Parisian pleasure-seekers by the nickname of 'Clarinette'. At that period of her career of pleasure, she lived in a cheap apartment in the Rue de Moscou, but having conducted her *little boat* with more than ordinary cunning, is now installed in the above aristocratic quarter with a house of fine furniture and a few louis in the money-box. A rich Pole is her chief booby, and she has a nobleman as second master, with a train of discreet admirers, who steal an hour in the daytime, and pay liberally for the *packet of sweets* they enjoy on the sly. Clara is short and dark, with a sallow skin, and presents a striking appearance beneath the gas, otherwise is rather inferior in breed and quality. The face is pretty, with a high, 'bumpy' forehead; but she is very plump, and not at all averse to a good tussle on a spring mattress, defying the most ardent combatant in the arena of love. Her library is well stocked with bawdy books, of which she is very fond, making up a neat collection of expensive obscene works, which her customers read while she is getting ready for them by performing the preliminary ablutions. She keeps herself very select, and as much aloof as possible from her colleagues in the art of whoring, although she is regularly visited by Laure Decroze, on Sapphic thoughts intent. The latter lady we noticed at length in a preceding paragraph. Clara's companion, guide, philosopher and friend is her female cook, who was once at the top of the tree and possessed horses and carriages, a fine establishment and lovers galore. But she got in the family way, was delivered of a child and went mad. During her enforced retirement to an establishment where straight waistcoats are all the 'go', she lost all, and now prepares the bidet for a more lucky moll. She is perfectly resigned to her fate, and is to be seen haggling for a pennyworth of onions, wearing a pair of her mistress's earrings.

Ernestine Desclauzas

THÉÂTRE DE LA RENAISSANCE

Woman is never too old to love, says some old proverb or other, and its truth is exemplified in the present instance. Although this lady is just forty, we can still urge all admirers of full-blown, autumnal beauty to pass a night or two in her company. She is tall and splendidly built, with black hair, hidden beneath a blonde wig, a turned-up nose with palpitating saucy nostrils and large, blue, voluptuous eyes, with dark lascivious circles beneath. Her bosom is of the largest size, and of excellent quality. She is a first-rate actress, and her successes on the stage are as numerous as in the boudoir. Being of a gay and jolly disposition she has never refused her favours to anyone who languished at her feet, so that she is still poor, but her good humour is the same as ever. Her 'fancy man' is a thin, little cornet player of Parisian concert orchestras. She is very loving and fond of babyish caresses, while the lovers of pederastic pleasure with the female will find themselves cordially welcomed and quickly hidden away in the deep furrow of her enormous, fascinating buttocks. Her real name is Marie Armand.

Marthe Devoyod

67 RUE JOUFFROY

This fair, English-looking, tall woman is only twenty-four years of age, and is rapidly advancing in public favour. She appears in genteel comedy at the Gymnase Théâtre, but her talents as an actress are slight, while her passion for the sport is intense. Her figure is rather angular and slender, but her teeth are white and sound, and her azure eyes are full of sparkling life. Her chief protector is a Russian, who is immensely rich, and who bought her virginity some two years ago for a fabulous sum. Her mother appropriated the prize, and now lives comfortably on the interest thereof, occasionally visiting her girl over whom she still exercises great influence. This matron considers she has done a great feat in watching over her daughter's maidenhead till she found the golden opportunity, and complacently tells the story of her unceasing vigilance, relating how she used to flog Marthe whenever she found her flirting, so we may consider that the St Petersburg swell did really get a membrane that was entirely intact.

Dezoder

13B RUE DES MATHURINS

The wiry frame of this dark-skinned pet, whose true name is Suzanne Jeandonnenc, has resisted the enervating effects of countless orgies, and every connoisseur who has a taste for unlimited lust, without a shade of refinement, will do well to worship at her shrine, especially as her low price makes her accessible to all. She boasts of a fine head of hair and shameless black eyes, with a sarcastic expression of countenance. She was formerly an actress at the Palais Royal, but her engagement terminating a few months back, she did not renew it, preferring to devote all her energies to the noble profession of which she is a most zealous member. We recommend our friends not to remain a whole night in her arms, as in the morning her breath is none of the sweetest.

Dinelli

90 RUE LAFAYETTE

She is of Italian descent, and her *piquante* style of beauty renders her very attractive. Her face is rather long, with a good-shaped, artful nose, a dark, warm skin, coal-black hair and a magnificent set of teeth, that she is rather too fond of showing. She is a good actress, and having a nice voice, has been as successful in comedy as in *opéra-bouffe*. She has been at the Gymnase and Bouffes-Parisiens, but is now at the Palais Royal. Her age is not more than five-and-twenty, and, although she has had a baby, her figure is neat and well-knit, with a sufficient amount of titties, placed rather high. She has a few diamonds, being passionately fond of jewels. Altogether a very charming piece, and would be without a single fault if she did not persist in wearing such dirty petticoats. All her lovers and friends were very much shocked a little while ago to hear that she had suddenly gone mad. She was immediately removed to a private asylum, and after a few weeks of judicious treatment has once more been restored to the eager arms of her clients.

Gabrielle Doria

7 RUE ROY

Here you may with pleasure view an exquisite little bit of stuff; a pert, enticing face; pouting lips, with pearly teeth; a compact figure and microscopic waist; small hands and feet; and the gift of enjoying her bedfellow with the greatest ecstasy. She was born at Genoa, and to prove noble birth takes the trouble to write her name with an apostrophe. A Corsican first debauched her, and she migrated to

Marseilles, where she appeared for about three years in the *cafés concerts* of that seaport. One fine morning, however, she grew tired of her music-hall and her Corsican lover, and fled to Paris, where she came out at second-rate theatres and finally landed at the Nouveautés. She was recommended on arriving to the famous Fanny Robert, who is sketched in this work, and the two priestesses of the Cyprian deity were fast friends for a time. Physically, our blonde little friend is all that can be desired; morally, she is blessed with a very even temper, but is slightly capricious. A foolish *amour* with a knight of the sock and buskin is just over, and Gabrielle, for a proportionate recompense, now bestows her favours on a rich member of the financial world. But she is very accessible all the same, and thoroughly enjoys a little bit *sub rosa*. Her own enchanting sex has charms for her too, and of late she has tried the pleasures of tribadism. A fire at her residence has made a small hole in her savings, so her scale of charges has been greatly reduced.

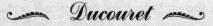

Ducouret

NOUVEAUTÉS THÉÂTRE

Tall; fair; Grecian nose; curiously-shaped mouth; good teeth; big, sleepy, luscious eyes; fine figure, all bubs and belly; the whole decorated with a dazzling assortment of diamonds. She is a fair specimen of a neck-or-nothing, dashing, lusty moll, but she is far too fond of actors. Her comrades are admitted with pleasure daily to a 'private view' of her charms, and she charges nothing for admission to her charming *theatre*, which is closed *every month*, and the rest of the time is like the Crystal Palace: 'Open Wet or Dry!' She prefers baritones to tenors, as they are stronger, and bigger across the chest. Tenors, she says, are only fit for finicking jobs, and light, fingering business.

~~ *Céline Dumont* ~~
CONCERT DE LA SCALA

A tall, dark, masculine woman of indefatigable gaiety. She is about twenty-six, and in the pursuit of fortune has travelled from her native town, Châteauroux, as far as the music-halls of Turkey and Russia. Her nerves seem toned down, however, and at the present moment she is contented with the hearty applause of Parisian audiences, and their more substantial homage at the foot of her couch. Her dwelling is remarkable for the strange disorder it presents, reminding the observer of a curiosity shop, as it contains a multitude of strange objects and curiosities that Céline has brought back from her travels. A splendid red and green parrot keeps watch over this museum, the mistress of which is ready at all times for the highest bidder.

~~ *Léa Dumont* ~~
41 RUE DE LISBONNE

On the first floor lives this fine, firm piece of flesh, and on the second used formerly to be found her inseparable friend, Glady, whom we mention in due course. Léa is a strong, fair, blue-eyed woman, full of health, with magnificent teeth and pale complexion; elastic, heaving, globular bubbies of the largest kind; chest and arms all firm, and of a milky whiteness; and a waist which is surprisingly small. The particular parts are adequate, and in fact this is one of the finest bodies for lust at present on the market. Perhaps she is a trifle too vulgar in her manner, although she is incessantly laughing, and is as gay as a lark. She has been tolerably well educated and possesses wit of the rough-and-ready sort. Her only fault is her lust for lesbianism, which she satisfies by a close intimacy with her bewitching neighbour – the two charmers sleeping together almost every night, with no other companion than Glady's little canine pet. But this Sapphic *liaison* will perhaps not be deemed such a very great crime by many of our curious readers. Besides, our experience bids us remark that these hot and strong friendships among trollops never last long, and perhaps at the moment we are writing these lines, our beauties are tired of munching each other's commodities, and have become sworn enemies – who shall say? The Dumont was born at Dijon in 1854, a respectable wholesale wine merchant being her father. When eighteen she came to Paris with a count, who took her maidenhead at the Hôtel de Louvre. One short year later she left her seducer, who was exhausted in every way, financial and otherwise. She then travelled as far as Constantinople, and lived six months with a bey, who is related to the ex-viceroy of Egypt. She managed to bleed the Turk for a large sum, and returned to the city of vice, where another nobleman gaily managed to devour his whole fortune with her, till in 1878, he was obliged to depart for the colonies, leaving his grass-widow and his creditors to mourn his loss. Léa swears that she will go to him one of these fine days, and marry the poor ruined wretch, but first she must economise some money out of the offerings bestowed at her shrine by the generous public. Her apartment is sumptuously furnished, and she knows by heart every one of Aretino's postures; so all Don Juans to whom a new position is a stimulator may ring at her door with the utmost confidence.

Pauline Duparc

Bouffes-Parisiens Théâtre

Liveliness and gaiety are here to be found united in the person of an agreeable young woman of the middle height. She is dark and stout, with finely furnished *corsage*. She has often been sent for by the *maquerelles*, but it will be found cheaper to apply to Pauline herself, who is far from being greedy after money. When her services are not needed at her theatre, she will pay a flying visit to her native city, Lyons, where she has a long list of admirers. Lesbian proclivities are fully developed in her lustful mind, and the insatiable Piccolo, whose biography we give in due course, is the favourite partner of these perverse debauches.

Georgina Dupont
MENUS-PLAISIRS THÉÂTRE

Another would-be actress, who merely stands behind the blazing line of footlights, so as to be able to display her flesh to the swells of the stalls. She is a young brunette, extremely stout, with a large pair of palpitating hemispheres that are always ready to burst out of her stays, and present their dark-brown nipples to the eager lips of her lovers. She is celebrated for employing her pliable charms for the enjoyment of the opposite sex, in a way which is fully expressed by the Latin verb: *mamillare*. Her dark eyes are as saucy as possible, and she carries out in full everything that their saucy glances promise, at very low rates.

Antoinette Duret
75 RUE DE LA BOETIE

We have already alluded to this florid Dutchwoman, who is remarkable for the enormous size of her bubbies. Unfortunately, they are no longer hard and firm, as Antoinette has been out some time and is getting on in age. She is known as 'La Tetonnière', and her tall, fine figure, blue eyes and well-furnished mouth must render her still attractive to all who admire fully-matured women. She is very hospitable, has a very handsomely furnished apartment, and is up to every salacious manoeuvre of the bedchamber.

Reneé Duroncay
7 RUE DE ROME

Once upon a time there were two golden-haired sisters, Renée and Léa, who earned a scanty living by washing the dirty linen of their fellow-creatures. Renée entered on the town, and understanding her business, soon became conspicuous in her sphere. She then engaged

Léa as her maid, and her young sister did not wait long before she also found a keeper, as there was nothing amiss in her person. The two girls now quarrelled, and one day they fought a regular battle together. The best of the two is Renée. She is an eccentric dresser, and makes up her face with a brown powder, so as to give an amber cast to her saucy countenance and bring into further prominence the meretricious glances of her bold, blue eyes. She is but an indifferent bedfellow, but the dexterity of her white hand is something to be enjoyed, all descriptions being powerless to convey her delicate power of touch. She has experienced severe strokes of fortune, and has but few friends, being as proud and arrogant when flush of money as she is subtle and humble when down on her luck. She has obliged the public at all prices and will take almost anything from those who try a fall with her. Léa, a showy girl, whose hair is as light as tow, has also had her share of hard knocks, and has tried the stage to increase her connection. She went to Russia about a year ago, and the fashionable world of Paris was pained to hear that she had gone mad when in St Petersburg. It is well known that the libertines of the north of Europe are fond of flagellation in all shapes and forms, and the terrible rod is actively wielded in England and Russia. Indeed, we are inclined to think that the country that invented the knout bears off the birching palm. Léa, for a considerable sum of money, had been induced by a colonel of the Imperial Guard to yield up her bum to his blows. She was hoisted and, the poor girl, subjected to the most fearful castigation with a leather strap and buckle. The shock to her nervous system was more than she could bear, and when unbound, with her backside pounded to a jelly, it was found that her reason had fled. She was placed in an asylum, but rapidly recovered, and at the time we write has returned to France, where her sister has met her and taken her to the South to pass the winter.

Berthe d'Eecloo

CONCERT DU XIXe SIÈCLE

This dark, finely moulded beauty is only twenty, and she sings charmingly, besides being a *pianiste* of no mean order. She first appeared at the Brussels music-hall, the Renaissance, in 1881, so that her adventures up to the present have not been very extraordinary. Her tastes are simple: she adores her work, her piano, flowers and birds, and the continual society of a vigilant mother. A rich lover in search of a tit-bit that has scarcely been nibbled at had better apply to the stern parent at once, as there are packs of wolves going about Paris to gobble up the little Red Riding Hoods, and Berthe is sure to be in great demand shortly.

Valentine d'Egbord

12 AVENUE D'ANTIN

The aged whores of Paris form what is called the 'Old Guard', because they never die and always surrender. Valentine is one of these, and she appears in our new Book of Revelations as a curiosity. Like a work of art, for marvellous preservation of remains of beauty, we treat her as such, and request visitors 'not to touch'. The proudest *phallus* must surely droop like the neck of a dead fowl at the sight of this playful creature of some thirty-six summers. Through the use and abuse of some cheap, golden dye, her hair has fallen off, never to grow again, and has been replaced by an expensive arrangement of a rich, door-mat colour. Her figure is slight, her eyes are blue, and her teeth are 'going, going, gone'. The motto on her notepaper is: 'D'Egbord d'abord!' (D'Egbord first!) This proud phrase is studded all over her harness, as she appears in regal splendour in a tremendous landau when her purse is full, which is very seldom nowadays. To sum up everything, we are bound to state that she received a most unkind wound from one of Cupid's arrows a little while ago, as the weapon was a poisoned one. But she has got over this syphilitic alarm, and for such men who admire the 'light of other days', however 'faded', may still prove an enjoyable jump – in the daytime, in a half-light, and with all her clothes on.

~ *Moïta Elias* ~

177 BOULEVARD HAUSSMANN

The life of this mellow piece would be worth publishing *in extenso*, could we but procure the true details, but the heroine is too cunning, and carefully hides the mysteries of her curious existence. We know that she has a real husband, who continually annoys her, and whom she is obliged to silence occasionally with the money she earns by the sweat of her backside. We are also aware that two of her most opulent admirers have died suddenly whilst in her company, under very suspicious circumstances. The first made a will in her favour, and started with her for a pleasant trip to Corsica. He dropped down dead on the steamboat, and Moïta was imprisoned on suspicion of poisoning, but was afterwards released. The next lover fell from his chair after breakfasting at her house, and never breathed again. Verdict: heart disease. Whether she be a Lucrezia Borgia or not is impossible to say, but we lately met a Lovelace of our friends, who, hungering for her body, feasted on her opulent charms for some months but took good care never to take bite or sup while beneath her roof. She calls herself Blanche d'Alfortville, and is also known as Moïta, simply; but we believe her correct denomination is as we have given it above. Her appearance is striking, as she is a stout, shapely brunette, with a fine development of womanly beauty: in front, she possesses grand bubbies, and behind, one of those marble arses that are always hard, firm and cool. All these delightful appendages are of enormous size, and the whole is set off by an expressive, laughing face, with black, staring, liquid eyes, bushy eyebrows, coal-black locks and a dazzling set of large teeth. Her private parts are firm, fat and tight, the mount being shaded by a profusion of curly black ringlets. She lives with a 'sister', about sixteen years of age, whom we shrewdly suspect to be her daughter. This young person, who is plain and who has nothing to recommend her, has just started in the fornicative way, but buyers of green fruit are chary in their offers. The stage has tempted this novice in the art of love, and she has got engaged at the Gymnase, where she figures in microscopic *rôles*, calling herself 'Netty'. Our readers will see that the Elias family will well return a flying favour, especially as Moïta, who has a neat income from her dead lovers, does not put a very big price on a real gentleman's pocket. Above all, listen calmly to her silly stories, and do not contradict her, as she is one of the most gigantic liars that ever went out a-whoring.

Gabrielle Elluini

224 BOULEVARD PEREIRE

Pauline Elluin is the real name of this professed woman of pleasure, and we are not going too far when we put her down as the richest moll in the world. One hundred thousand pounds sterling is about the strength of her fortune, and she spends her loose cash right royally; the best of everything being hardly good enough for her. Her villa, at the above address, is a little gem, eight thousand pounds being the amount paid to the upholsterer for hangings and mural decoration only. She has got an aesthetic studio, the hand that so nimbly handles *paint brushes of all kinds* turning out occasionally a wretched daub, that kind friends and flatterers extol to the skies. Next we must admire a private chapel, where Gabrielle has *fits of piety*. Her horses and carriages are perfect in their way, and her liveries are gorgeous and glaring. She is passionately fond of diamonds, and possessed a rare collection of gems of the first water, which she used to wear studded all over her person, till she was one blaze of jewels, from her diadem to her shoe-buckles. The scented garters, fringed with rare old lace, that encircled her shapely limbs, were studded with the same precious stones. In person she resembles a ruddy, healthy, vulgar, Irish beauty. The features are bold and square cut; her large eyes are dark-blue; her fleshy lips discover strong and white teeth, while her voice is hoarse and her manner overbearing. Her portly figure is always decked out in insane toilettes, of staring hue, that are a month ahead of the fashions, and we have seen her hissed out of a public restaurant on account of the eccentricity of her bejewelled get-up. All this is done to attract attention, and she had even gone so far as to affect great enthusiasm for the Buonapartist cause, so that by giving political *soirées* at her house she may be talked about in the lying Parisian press. She heads the list of every public subscription, and it is generally said that her principal lover – a big financier of the Bourse – only kept her as an advertisement of his wealth, and that he did not care a straw either for her society or her charms. Some years ago, for she is going on for thirty, she paraded her person and her regalia on the public stage, appearing at several theatres, but her talents being small, she only met with failure in the histrionic capacity. Bad times on the Stock Exchange recently played the deuce with her protector's pocket and Gabrielle was obliged to give him up. She thought of retiring from active warfare, and married a young actor, named Abel, who had been a pet of moneyed dames all his life. The honeymoon at Nice lasted but a few days, as the wife rushed into print and by a letter in the newspapers let everybody know that she had been cheated out of her right, as the *meat* that was to satisfy her legitimate appetite was *diseased*. She complained bitterly of her disappointment, stating that she had refused the hand of princes to espouse a man in her own sphere. This pretty quarrel has since been patched up, and now Elluini, having sold off her diamonds, means to live happy ever after and have plenty of children – if she is lucky.

Marie Estradère

BOUFFES-PARISIENS THÉÂTRE

An insignificant, slight, chestnut beauty, with good features, and a dimple in her chin. She has been the friend of the public for many years, and still looks the same as ever. She is known by the peculiar nickname of 'Boule de Gomme', which is a favourite sweetmeat, because she is never so happy as when she has got a fine *sugar stick* between her lips. Always ready for any mortal thing, she has a select private collection of old married men of dirty tastes, who call upon her in the daytime to gratify their most lascivious dreams. In one afternoon she has been known to divest herself of clothing, and run up and down a pair of steps, while an elderly amateur was onanising himself beneath; then she has flogged one of the members of the Senate; and has wound up by orally polluting a dramatic author, who had promised her a good part in a new *opéra-bouffe*. A little while ago she was invited to a ball, given at a fashionable club, and was seen to disappear several times, but always with a fresh partner.

Some inquisitive guests took the liberty of following her, and it was found that she had led her victims to her brougham, and esconced therein, employed her fair hand to receive their manly libations. For the accommodating shake of her wrist she charged five louis, and was driving a roaring trade till the gentlemen put an end to her vagaries and sent her home with a flea in her ear.

Aimée Eymard

Nouveautés Théâtre

A fresh arrival in the Parisian world of debauchery, but all the more to be prized on that account, as the varnish of youth has not been damaged, chipped or *licked off*. She had not played many nights before a rich Russian paid the forfeit stipulated in her engagement, and took her away, to enjoy this gypsy sprite all to himself. The dark darling boasts of a pointed nose; curious, little, piercing Chinese eyes; slight figure; and small feet. The rakes of the Boulevards mutter, as the moisture of letchery runs down their beards, that she is extremely hot in her elastic *crater*, and that she possesses a power of contraction that is probably unique. Her philanthropic device is 'J'aime qui m'aime' ('Who loves me, I love.') Aimée is passionately fond of horseflesh and possesses a fine brougham and pair of steppers as black as the hair that protects her pussy.

Celestine Faivre

3, Place du Théâtre Français

Her age is a mystery. She might be thirty or forty or perhaps not so old. Sometimes she is fair and sometimes dark, according to her fancy. Her teeth are false; her eyes are of the sigh-away, die-away blue kind; the nose is pointed and the general tone is sad. Celestine goes in for melancholy, because it suits her style. The figure is neat, with a moderate amount of bust, the legs are long and the arms are thin. She is a good actress and is now at the Folies-Dramatiques Théâtre. Till within the last few years she graced the provinces with her presence, when she was known as Madame Diepdalle. Her temper is generally far from smooth, but she is a painstaking bedfellow. This lady will certainly not please everybody, but as she has a large connection, we may credit her with having secret nocturnal qualities, as Frenchmen do not, as a rule, throw their money into a whore's lap unless she knows her trade and can produce pleasure in exchange for pelf.

Odette Farna

17 RUE DE TREVISE

Here is another tartlet who has not been too much hacknied. She first blossomed into favour at the Châtelet Théâtre last winter, and is already a valuable acquisition to the whoring army of our city. She is young, thin, and her hair is of the hue that is vulgarly called 'carrotty'. As yet, her miniature, snowy bosom is not quite developed, but a few years' business will soon fatten her up and make her a perfect piece. Anyhow she is a convenient little lass, and there is a certain latent charm in the awkward way in which she takes her place by the side of her suitor for the night that is very refreshing to the *connoisseur* of venal beauties, after the enervating and scientific mauling of bouncing old meaty whores.

Camille Faure

32 RUE DE BERLIN

This courtesan is a time-defying bag of bones, in the style of the evergreen Delphine Delizy, but not one quarter as pretty. But as she is always provided with rich admirers, we must suppose that her beauty lies hidden somewhere near her backside. She is a tiny, dark, skinny little minx, with a fine pair of black eyes, one of which has gone wrong, as its protecting eyelid droops somewhat. It is impossible to tell her age, but she has been on the town ever since we can remember, and her temper is none of the sweetest. Our honest advice is: let this little cat alone.

Isabelle Féraud

81 Avenue Montaigne

One of the tip-top maids of honour at the court of jolly old King Priapus, she has feathered her nest considerably during the few years she has been trafficking with her shapely body. She was born in Chili, and used to sing at the music-halls there. Her command of the Spanish language has earned for her charms the substantial gifts of the South American colony of Paris. Independent now, she can afford to pick and choose her customers, and she only responds to the challenge of wealthy men. The money or present you are to give engrosses her whole thoughts whilst she is in the very act, and makes her rather a frigid victim when the manly instrument is at work in the sheath provided by nature's kind laws. She is extremely pretty: short, fair hair, that owes much of its beauty to chemical washes; good bust and fine legs, although these ivory columns are a little too short in proportion to the upper part of her figure. Her large blue eyes look upon her admirers with the most innocent stare, but when she opens her coral lips, some part of the charm is dispelled, as Isabelle possesses a rough and disagreeable voice. A Prussian prince has knocked an ugly child out of her, and he makes her a liberal yearly allowance. Nothing pleases her better than an excursion to a bawdy-house, when she treats all the women there and plays all kinds of lesbian frolics, finishing up by submitting to the caresses of the first passer-by, who will perhaps endow her with a few francs only, not esteeming her more than the usual inmates of the house where she finds herself. She then runs downstairs, laughing till the tears come into her eyes, and, throwing the paltry silver coins into the air, will exclaim: 'That imbecile has just had Isabelle Féraud, and does not know it!' She was the heroine this year of a strange wager. A young man about town, a proficient in the art of labial onanism, swore that he could extract a flower from the innermost recesses of a lady's genital organs without injuring the blossom. A supper was given at the Café Anglais to which Isabelle was invited, and a gardenia being inserted in her private parts and carefully packed away out of sight, she was hoisted on to the table. The wager was now decided *coram populo*, to the delight of all concerned, and particularly of the fair and shameless Féraud. The young libertine began to exercise the voluptuous contractions of his lips and tongue, and a roar of applause greeted the saucy scamp as he lifted his flushed face from between her thighs and triumphantly showed his sticky moustache and the gardenia between his teeth. Its petals, now smelling doubly sweet (?), were without a fold. He had won his bet. The key of her bedchamber, in pure gold, hangs on her watch-chain, in readiness for genuine money offers. Last year a young swell, not overburdened with cash or brains, gave one thousand pounds for a night in her arms. He is now ruined entirely and parades around Paris without boots.

Fillion

72 RUE LAUGIER

Some people object to paying a high price for meat, and enjoy themselves greatly when they know that the bill will not be a heavy one. To these sober rakes we commend the come-at-able young girl now under notice. She is tall, slender and dark, with brown eyes, and is very pretty and very warm, clinging round her companion for the nonce, like the ivy round the oak. She appeared on the stage for a short spell last winter, and was literally bombarded with bouquets and letters. Strange to say, she does not care for *ducking* and *diving*, or any of the flowery you-tickle-me-and-I'll-tickle-you sort of games that are put in practice by most Parisian votaries of Venus. No, what she wants is the old-fashioned Adam-and-Eve style of copulation, all give-and-take and no cheating.

Mab de Folligny

19 AVENUE DE VILLIERS

The arrival on the Parisian asphalt of this peculiar priestess of Venus created considerable excitement some eighteen months back. Let our readers imagine the dwarflike charms of a vivacious Arab girl: hands that drive the glove-makers mad; waist that would make a wasp jealous; two brown globes, as hard as apples, forming proper adornments in front; a sweet, impertinent nose; large velvety-black eyes; and, to crown all, hair of the colour of dead gold. Her limbs are small-made, but exquisitely-shaped, and she can offer to the lovers of posterior charms an arse like that of Alcibiades, brown and firm, so that in front she is like a woman and behind like a boy. Mab, who is a Jewess, was born at Bône (Algeria), where we are told that her family is well respected. Our charmer has brought with her to Paris all the indolent ways of the Orientals. Like a sleek panther she curls herself into a little heap of loveliness, and rolls her warm, fragrant body on her divan with the fascinating grace of a serpent. Her whole demeanour reminds one of the East, and her passionate, fiery nature makes her a most enticing morsel for a winter's night, especially as she does not spare herself, but freely offers every part of her handsome frame to the different desires of her capricious customers. Her flight from home was due to the heat of her nature, that renders more than one man necessary to satisfy her lust, and she appeared at Lyons about two years ago with a lover. That city went mad about her, but she was too fickle, as the officers of the garrison can testify. Then, coming to Paris, she found a gentleman who was about to buy her a villa, horses, carriages, etc., but a panic on the Bourse put an end to dreams of rapid fortune, and Folligny, as she calls herself, had to start in the profession of love. She is a nymphomaniac, or to put things more politely, suffers from a nervous malady that the doctors know well, and which manifests itself in a maddening desire for copulation. Her fingers are always irritating the rosy bud which is the seat of all sensual desire in the female, and even when the male retires, after having bedewed her womb with a beneficent shower, she remains panting, delirious, dissatisfied still, with the furious masturbating manoeuvres going on incessantly. She only sleeps a few hours nightly, her uterine fury preventing slumber, and all the hydrate of chloral and bromide of potassium in the world are powerless to give her relief. One night, for a strong man, with Mab, is a rare treat that should not be missed. The poor girl is not mercenary, and never talks scandal about her fellow workers. She is greatly sought after, and always accessible, so that she has got a great fornicating future before her, unless galloping consumption claims her for its prey.

Marie Folliott

9 Rue de l'I'sly

A glorious blonde, with a white skin and pleasing features. She is very alluring in her manner, and thoroughly insinuates herself into the favours of her man. Her bosom is a splendid sight; the globes being beyond the normal size, and tipped with two sweet, rosy nipples. The warmth of her bubbies is a better recipe for impotency than any stimulus or provocative the whole medical faculty can furnish. She can wake to life the fleeting, sluggish spirits, and give to age itself the vigour even of youth; and he who rises from her bed finds himself only tired, not cloyed or satiated. Unfortunately, there is a slight blot on this otherwise perfect picture. The poor creature is slightly lame in the left hip. We believe the infirmity arises from a severe fall, caused by a carriage accident. Her female friends, who envy her good looks and ladylike bearing, say that she suffers from venereal disease. Marie was formally an assistant in a milliner's shop, but her beauty singled her out for the attack of the seducer, and she soon had to depend on the public for a living. She has been in high keeping, and is the mother of a handsome boy.

Lucy Gaudet

53 Rue Vivienne

A so-called actress of the Variétés Théâtre, earnestly recommended to such of our readers whose *natural purse* is better furnished with material for giving pleasure than their pocket is with cash. Lucy is twenty-four, slim and tall, black hair, a good figure and large blue eyes, with an innocent look in her cerulean orbs. She is as quiet as a lamb and quite as obedient. Slow lovers need not hurry themselves with her, as she will extend herself in the pretty, passive, horizontal position and wait without a murmur till the most *blasé* Don Juan chooses to cry, 'Hold, enough!'

Juliette Grandville

19 BOULEVARD DE LA MADELEINE

A magnificent dark woman, above the ordinary size, with all her massive charms in proportion. She is of a very libidinous disposition, as the brown half-moons beneath her bright eyes can testify. Many are the pranks she has played with her own sex in bed, where she is as lascivious as a goat, but her tastes in that direction do not present a scandalous itching for the male sex. The man she most cares for is one who can boast of superior size and strength in the part that most delights the weaker sex. In short, this mature lady of about twenty-seven years of age is a most juicy piece, and her appearance on the stage, for she is a second-rate actress at the Palais Royal and Variétés, always sends an erotic thrill through the *habitués* of the stalls. Among her principal *amours* may be quoted Dupuis, of the Variétés, a sturdy 'masher' we have already mentioned, and her 'mistress', with whom she has enjoyed many a Sapphic scramble, Marie Magnier, who is fully described in another part of this work. Grandville is one of the kindest instruments of joy in Paris, but if she should fall in love with a man or woman she is deeply, unreasonably jealous for a time. She is about the only woman we have ever met with who can exercise affection for both sexes at one and the same time. She is often Sappho by day and Messalina by night, rushing eagerly to the arms of her masculine adorer with the glorious traces of some girlish victim's excitement fresh on her feverish ruby lips.

Jeanne Granier

RENAISSANCE THÉÂTRE

After cataloguing so many stupid whores, whose only talents consist in their automatic knowledge of provoking emission and the complete abandon of every orifice of their finely built bodies, it is quite refreshing to stumble across a really witty and vivacious woman, whose society is agreeable even when we are resting after our ardent combats in the good cause. Granier is a clever and

vivacious actress of comic opera, and off the stage is as full of fun,
malice and laughter as a boarding-school miss. She was born in
1852, but time has dealt lightly with her slim frame, and she does
not look more than twenty-three. It was late in the day, and only
after she had been very successful on the stage, that she opened her
legs to the general crowd of promiscuous lovers, and there was a
hushed-up case of abortion some few years back, her first lover
having forgotten that an actress, the slave of the public, must never
be allowed to get in the family way, and that her partners in the
game of *push pin* should know how to withdraw gracefully at a
certain moment. This alarm did not prevent her giving birth to a
pretty little girl, who is her idol. The most amusing side of Granier's
versatile disposition consists in the unaffected childishness of her
ways. She is fond of playing with dolls, of which she has a splendid
collection, and when she writes a letter will illustrate it with many
sketches, which are sometimes of a gaily obscene description. She is
a brunette, with a wiry, healthy frame; small, piercing eyes; a saucy,
pointed nose; and splendid mouth, with a thick underlip that looks
like a velvet cushion to lay kisses on. Her private house, in the
Avenue Wagram, is a most comfortable cosy nest for copulation,
where all real good-fellows with well-lined purses are greeted as
they ought to be. One of her first lovers was a celebrated man about
town and duellist, who used to give her very little money, and beat
her till she got quite used to being black and blue all over and
declared that if he left her she would really miss her daily thrashing.
He got married, and her principal lover up to within the last few
months was a young prince of famous Buonapartist descent. This
amour did not prevent her receiving the usual run of casual lovers,
and she submitted gaily to the erotic experiments of wealthy, but
blasé amateurs. Granier's only fault is a weakness for the bottle:
absinthe and champagne being the usual beverages before going on
the stage, and also when returning to her bedroom, where the real
work of the night begins. We find no trace of active tribadism in the
past life of this foolish virgin, but she has often been tempted to
respond to the slobbering advances of rich Sapphos, who have given
her large sums to be allowed to kiss her clitoris.

Gallayx
GYMNASE THÉÂTRE

This little, black tickler will evidently not excite rapturous enthusiasm
in the breast of the searcher after novelty and extraordinary beauty,
but will content the sober lover of hearty sensual enjoyment at a low
price. Gallayx is twenty-two, with hair like the raven's wing, white
teeth, vivacious eyes, and a charm of conversation that is greater
than her natural loveliness. She has never made herself too cheap, so
that the customer may in all safety beg from her the favour of a
night's lodging.

Gabrielle Gauthier
9 RUE NOTRE DAME DE LORETTE

A fine, showy, dark woman of about thirty years of age, with firm,
globular, heaving breasts of abundant size. The backside beauties
are of the same massive build, and the fall in the back is of peculiar
beauty, forcing the amateur to *take her in the rear*, but not in Italian
style. Her eyes are black and fiery; the nose straight, small and
sensual; the lips of coral hue; the teeth white and strong, with ruby
gums that are a sure sign of health and pureness of blood. She is
always laughing, and full of quip, crank and repartee – but allowing
no joke against the Republic, as she is a fanatic in politics, and
believes that all men are equal. She has had sufficient experience,
however, to find that no two men are alike. She has lived for many
years with a journalist of communistic tendencies, and he seems to
be a rare socialist, as far as his mistress is concerned, for she appeals
to the bounty of the public to contribute towards the payment of
her dressmaker's bill, and her lord and master does not seem to care.
Her handsome mouth, with its irritating shade of black down, may
be warmly recommended for its complaisant kisses, while her robust
mount will be found covered with sturdy patches of black hair, and
this hardy growth will be found beneath and even behind. The
strength in bed of this female Samson will be found exhilarating in

the extreme, as Gabrielle, a thorough adept in the rites of Venus, likes the genuine article, and can show a frame that has not been enervated by unnatural excesses. She is an excellent actress, and is generally sought after to play laughing chambermaids in big dramas. She varies her existence by a little mild proxenetism, being always able to introduce you to some unfledged girl of her friends, and she has no scruple in accepting a liberal percentage of their spermatic salary. Although, as we have said, she is no adept of the lesbian crowd, Gauthier likes to look at and handle for a few seconds the *cockle-shells* of her companions, and comparing notes, will deftly raise her neat petticoats and show her own dark *watermark*. May our readers see her at one of those moments, and like Paris of old, be requested to bestow the apple.

~ *Conchita Gélabert* ~

BOUFFES-PARISIENS THÉÂTRE

Fresh as a rose; well made; of the middle size; fair complexion; and affecting an air of modesty. She has a beautiful aquiline nose, with a remarkable pair of immense, wondering blue eyes. Her foot is as small as Cinderella's, and her hands are as tiny as those of a baby. She was born at Madrid in 1857, but has been brought up in France. The second prize at the Conservatoire was bestowed upon her when she finished her musical education, and she appeared on the stage as principal actress of *opéra-bouffe*. Her sweet voice and pretty ways drew the men after her virgin tail at once, but a stern mamma kept watch over those secret charms, that as yet had only been profaned by the innocent finger of awakening desire, and the awkward caresses of her school companions. She had often noticed her professors of music polluting themselves while they gave her lessons, which they would have preferred to be of a different kind, but she had escaped positive defloration till her appearance behind the footlights. An enthusiastic spectator made her an offer of his hand, and as he was wealthy, mamma forced little Conchita to consent, and everything was ready, when the bridegroom absconded. This sad flight led to an action for breach of promise of marriage, the damages being laid at some fabulous amount. Mother and daughter failed in court, so the old lady lost no time in selling her girl to a dried-up chip of a man – an old banker, from Toulouse. He is a widower, with six ugly daughters, and he is very fond of his purchase, and fearfully jealous. But the tiny, Spanish baby-woman often gives him the slip, and engulfs a younger and stronger morsel than that which the debile money-grubber carries in his suspensory. Gélabert has had a severe miscarriage, and she now suffers from continual loss of her urine, which she is powerless to stop, necessitating the use of plugs of various descriptions.

Alice Giesz

17 RUE DE MADRID

It would never be believed that this small, thick-set wench was an actress, as she looks like a country girl, fresh from the fields, and a rosy, buxom, healthy one too. She is stout and fair; with a big mouth, thoroughly furnished with fine, pearly teeth, and a clear complexion. It is wonderful how she has kept her freshness, as no woman has ever enjoyed such a full swing of pleasure as she has. She first appeared in the world of whoredom as the concubine of Gill, the political caricaturist, who is now rotting away in a lunatic asylum. Then a reporter became her principal keeper. But he died young, and she went on the stage at the Gymnase. There the siren wove her toils round the son of the manager. Papa died, and our astute little moll captured the youth and his inheritance, kept him away from his family, and thoroughly enjoyed herself. Alice has one or two lovers for her own private use, and pays right royally for her amusement, as she is really perfectly insatiable. At the time we write, she is expending her remarkable energy in ruining the son of her late director, whom she keeps locked up and entirely under the charm of the voluptuous excitement that exudes from her every pore.

Gilberte

NOUVEAUTÉS THÉÂTRE

This young lady is below the ordinary size, and about twenty-seven years of age, with a provoking, crooked mouth. Her hair is of the most beautiful chestnut brown, and she has the additional advantage of a well-shaped neck and snowy arms. A cheap hour may be advantageously passed in her arms, as she will be satisfied with a couple of gold pieces, and in the tender preludes of bliss, is beyond description.

Gilberte

BOUFFES-PARISIENS THÉÂTRE

A thirty-six-year-old actress, with limbs moulded like a Venus. She has been many years on the boards, and her choice proportions have often been shown beneath the limelight, when she represented the Fairy of Good or Evil, as the case might be. She is very dark, with a fine set of teeth and a slight suspicion of moustache at the corners of a most enticing mouth. She takes great care of her handsome person, which deserves a minute examination that is sure to call forth a thorough exploration of *all parts*. She has had the luck to have been several times in keeping, but like most creatures of her class, has never put by for the proverbial rainy day and is therefore a facile, submissive victim for the moneyed devotee to lechery.

Gioja

12 AVENUE DU BOIS DE BOULOGNE

If a courtesan is bedizened with diamonds, the moth allured by their flame is supposed to pay extra, so that gentlemen who object to paying interest on other people's capital had better steer clear of this regal harlot. She is a magnificent, tall, blonde creature, and when in ballroom adjustment looks a perfect picture. Italy was her birthplace, but the bulk of her colossal fortune is derived from the liberalities of a Scottish duke who has just been selling his wonderful collection of artistic curiosities. Gioja has taken good care of the bright English sovereigns that her keeper bestowed upon her some years ago, before his marriage, and she has maintained her *prestige* intact. It is extremely difficult to get into her bed without an introduction and plenty of cash in advance, her couch having frequently creaked beneath the weight of royal debauchees.

Glady
17 VILLA SAID

This is the friend of Léa Dumont, of whom we have already spoken at length, and she is one of the most ferocious tribades in Paris. She is as pale as an aristrocratic lady of fashion, with chestnut hair, worn in plain bands on her forehead, and her eyes are like those of a cat, being as green and deep as the sea. Her mouth is superb, with full, luscious lips of rosy tint, and teeth of alabaster whiteness. Indeed, such eyes and such teeth are enough to make the fortune of any woman, and Glady does a deal of business and earns plenty of money. Her person is slight, well built, and she is very graceful in her manner. She was born in an obscure country village some twenty-six years ago, and at the age of fifteen was debauched by a yokel in a field of rising corn. She then started for Paris, where she began as an artificial flower maker, and her progress in the capital is the ordinary story of the rich whore, who passes from under the dirty body of the counter-jumper to the arms of a blue-chinned actor, finally being encircled between the legs of some wealthy scion of a noble house. The cheques and banknotes poured into her coffers and Glady furnished a magnificent apartment, in the house where lived Dumont, with a golden bedroom, pink satin and green velvet boudoir, bathroom with mosaic floor and walls of looking-glass, and dressing-room, all draped with blue satin. But her reckless extravagance and dissolute life soon drove her into debt, and now without means, the luxurious surroundings having vanished, she lives in more quiet and sober style, at the address we have given above. She is a good musician, swims like a fish, fences and shoots like a duellist and rides horseback like another celebrated Sappho, who is a real empress. A fervent priestess of Venus, she is capable of offering twenty sacrifices in one night on the altar of love, and all the money she gets from the men, she offers to any woman who takes her fancy, keeping herself foolishly poor. She is a convivial companion, and stands on no ceremony with her friends and lovers – the old peasant blood often declaring itself by an outburst of choice oaths and blasphemous expressions. The horses and carriages she has had, the fine clothes she has worn and the society of educated suitors she has enjoyed have never converted this rough-and-ready prostitute into a lady. Glady drinks like a fish, her favourite tipple being a priceless old cognac, of which a glass is gaily proffered to all comers – from the high-born lover in search of enjoyment, down to the humble postman who brings her love letters. Her chest is weak, showing signs of consumption, so that if Glady does not refrain from excessive indulgence with her own sex, and drop the brandy-flask entirely, she will not much longer be able to charm her numerous admirers.

Jeanne Goby

8 Place Bréda

A short lady, who has figured to advantage on the Parisian stage, appearing in light comedy. She has fine, blonde, silky hair; good eyes; charming teeth; and a pretty nose of the Grecian cast. Her figure is neat and genteel, and her general bearing most ladylike. Her youth and beauty have enabled her to captivate a foolish boy, who has just come into his fortune and title. As we write, we hear rumours in the smoking-rooms of our clubs of a marriage and we should not be at all surprised if it were true; the little devil always having been noted for keeping her own counsel, and hiding all trace of her numerous *amours*, has passed for a prude among those who only knew her superficially.

～ Alice Gordon ～
16 RUE VÉZELAY

Of Scotch descent, her grandfather having settled in Belgium; so Alice, now that she trafficks with her charms, has adopted the name of these respectable ancestors. Her father and mother keep a pastrycook's shop under the shadow of the University of Brussels, and it was there that this randy minx was brought up, serving behind the counter till just about nineteen. At that age she allowed her maidenhead to become the prey of a sturdy student of the neighbouring temple of learning. The task was easy, as Madame Gordon candidly confesses that she was always a vicious little cat. The differences of sex had troubled her budding brain from the earliest age, and the sight of the nurses in the Bois de la Cambre holding out their charges to pee, taught her that a little boy had something different between his legs from that which she had, that which felt so 'funny' when she rubbed between her thighs in the morning. But Brussels being one of the most depraved cities in Europe, considering its size, it was not long before the curious maiden became fully enlightened on all the points that puzzled her, by stumbling across a bookseller, who incautiously let her have the run of his stock. When we say that the capital of Belgium is the recognised centre for the publication of all the erotic works of the French language, our readers will become sufficiently enlightened as to the studies of our future harlot. She started with devouring *Gamiani*, then gobbled up the celebrated *Portier*, and perused with feelings of mingled horror and lust the bloody orgies of the ferocious Marquis de Sade, in the pages of *Justine and Juliette*. Her well-thumbed library was hidden beneath her mattress, and in her bed, moist with her fragrant perspiration and stained with the ruby fluid of the first signs of puberty, she would enjoy these erotic classics, reading them *with one hand*. Her precocious desires led her to take long walks with boyish sweethearts, and many a luscious kiss and timid 'feel' did she enjoy, till her confessor put a very indiscreet question to her. She humbly avowed that she had allowed herself to be 'kissed'. The salacious priest eagerly asked 'Where?' This was quite enough for Alice, who ran home, and getting a little apprentice into her room, filched a bottle of anisette out of the shop. The tiny white jacketed and white-capped turnspit was placed on his knees, and allowed to lick the sweet liqueur from the lips of her centre of bliss. Many a bottle was used up this way, and innumerable are the tales Alice will tell of her girlish attempts to provoke what was and has always been to her the *summum bonum* of earthly felicity. After the student, a Belgian nobleman was received in her arms, and the result was a charming little boy, who is now about six years old. In 1878 she came to Paris, and put herself under the wing of Delphine Delizy, who launched her on the troubled sea of prostitution. A keeper was found in the person of a wealthy member of a most exclusive club, who is still with her, but he is middle-aged, and so staid and precise that his concubine takes every opportunity she can to change her bedfellow. The effects of her early training have not been effaced from her mind, and she dreams of falling madly in love with some Byronic, Satanic, Swinburnic personage, who shall hold her in his power, and treat her like one of de Sade's heroines. She would like to be beaten, humiliated, and loved besides; indeed she hardly knows what she really desires, but it must be some strange, new, horrible, refined debauchery. In the meantime she indulges to excess in the pleasures of 'minette', but men, not women, frolic with her, and indulge in the game of *soixante-neuf*. Sometimes she will visit, with a chosen band of friends, the tip-top bawdy-houses of Paris, and all present, in primitive nudity, will try to vie with the Roman emperors. Alice is of middle height and looks thin till undressed, but her beautiful bosom and plump, firm bottom soon draw a cry of astonished delight from the lucky amateur. Her figure is incomparably fine, and her skin is of wonderful texture, causing her robust thighs to feel like satin to the touch. Her hair and eyes are dark brown, the eyebrows are black, and she has a lovely mouth, with a most sensual upper lip. Her age is now about twenty-six, and she is just the piece required for a downright reckless rake, who wants a mistress who will refuse him absolutely nothing but cheerfully bow to his every whim, even when he tries to realise, as much as possible, the ardent but cruel pastimes of a Tiberius or a Caligula.

Jane Hading

GYMNASE THÉÂTRE

Jeannette Hadingue is the true name of this mercenary enchantress, and she first saw the light at Marseilles in 1856 or 1859. Her father was a successful provincial actor, and his daughter has been all her life on the stage. She can play any mortal thing, and has been flourishing in *opéra-bouffe* lately in Paris and Brussels, as the Hebrew manager, to whom we alluded when speaking of Brindeau, made her his concubine for a time and tried to cram her down the throat of the public. She is saucy and bold, and thinks too much of herself even to please a Parisian audience. After the opera is over, she is worthy of notice, when her supple figure and expressive countenance, with lustrous black eyes, draw substantial proofs of admiration from the numerous rakes who are never so pleased as when they sleep with an actress. This lady is just as salacious as all French trollops are.

Maria Henry

7 AVENUE VICTOR HUGO

A tall, lithe, energetic brunette, with her hair died to a golden hue and with good brown eyes. She is about twenty-eight, but we are bound to say that she does not look her age. She was formerly an 'extra lady' at a little theatre in the gardens of the Champs Elysées, which is now pulled down. It was there that her meagre legs, without calves, first excited the risibility of Parisian fast-men, and business was so bad with her that she only possessed one chemise, and was obliged to remain in bed on Sunday mornings while her charwoman washed and dried the embroidered shift that comprised in itself her entire stock of body-linen. One summer's evening, a daring groom or stable-help climbed up to her dressing-room window, and the pair, after a paltry bargain had been struck, went hard at work, forgetting to heed the call-boy's warning cry. The stage waited, and there was a fearful row when the manager, mounting to the little room, found the flash gentleman seated in an armchair, with eyes half-closed and dress disarranged, engaged in deep *conversation* with Maria. She was using her *jawing tackle* and he was only *listening*. The insubordinate actress was dismissed the theatre there and then, with a hearty kick in the back part of her 'tights', but the acquaintance of that night was so delighted at the scientific manner in which she *wielded her tongue* that he induced her to form an association with him and employ her powers of *elocution*, a great deal for her benefit and a little for his. He became her coachman, her bully and the architect of her fortune. She is now a rich woman, and lives in a superb apartment, with furniture of price and a comfortable balcony. When disengaged, she goes to the minor theatres, accompanied by her fancy-man and her maid, but as she does not mind to what lengths she goes to satisfy her numerous clients, she may probably be thought worthy of a visit by those who demand entire resignation from the woman they employ to carry out their voluptuously selfish demands.

Lilia Herman

56 Rue de Naples

We have already spoken of this pretty morsel, when sketching Rosine Bloch, whose cousin she is. Lilia is a young actress of the Renaissance Théâtre, and the type of a pretty blonde Jewess with a fresh complexion and a large healthy mouth – which is often put to base uses by both her male and female friends. Need we say more?

Marguerite Heumann

6 Rue de Turin

A Jewess, but with no objection to a bit of Christian flesh – not in Shylock's way; she chooses her's lower. The typical, aquiline nose of her race is situated between fine piercing black eyes that light up the swarthy complexion of her handsome face, which is surrounded by lustrous raven locks. Her stature is short; the bust broad and robust, splendidly furnished with a heavy pair of semi-globes that make one's fingers itch to press them, while her firm, rounded arms will encircle her lover's neck in a velvety embrace. She is a tolerable actress, and we have seen her play Cupid, filling out her fleshings to bursting with muscular legs and thighs that needed no padding. Her followers are all of the sixty per cent persuasion, and when she has got an engagement, the theatre is so crammed with the disciples of Moses, that it looks and smells like a synagogue.

Laure Heymann

4 RUE LAPÉROUSE

Anyone can see from the wild, agitating stare of her lovely blue eyes that Laure is an insatiable receiver of the precious balm of manhood, and while the student of medicine might murmur 'hysteria', the hunter after new sensation in the accommodating world of whore-dom will hunger for the wild delights to be found in the arms of a glorious beauty with a strong nervous development. This member of the demi-monde has never spared her body in any shape or way, and she is up to every move on the board of love. She is any age between twenty and thirty, and is warm blonde, hailing from the French colonies, and possessing all the luscious qualities of those in whose veins has descended a drop of negro blood. Her size is just about the proper medium height, and all her charms – front and back – are in symmetrical proportion. Her hair is of a rich golden tint, without chemical aid, and her pomegranate lips disclose an admirable set of teeth. Laure has had adventures without number, and has been several times located in beautiful homes, always under the protection of thoroughbred gentlemen. The cause of her many quarrels with her wealthy lovers has been her lasting fondness for lesbian diver-sions. The Countess Mimi Pegère, surnamed the 'Comtesse Noire', who deserted her station in society to become a venal Venus, has long been her devoted friend and indefatigable tribade; and it is a glorious sight to see the fair Laure locked in the serpentine embrace of the lecherous little Sappho, who is as black as a coal, being a native of Haiti. This pleasant view and contrast of their two skins, one so white and the other so black, has been vouchsafed to many; and during the last two winters the five o'clock *tableaux vivants* of the volcanic

Heymann have been the subject of talk and cause of sly erection in all our clubs. Every man of fashion has made at least one ante-prandial visit to her saloons and, as we write, we hear that Laure has got at least *six* accredited lovers, without counting the numerous haphazard meetings that each day brings forth. A member of the English diplomatic service, brother of a well-known professional beauty; a French nobleman; and a magnate of the Stock Exchange, are the principal partners of her bed. Laure earns as much money as she likes, but she spends fabulous amounts in clothing her divine form, with the sole object of creating envy in the hearts of her less fortunate sisters who thrive on the merry game of prostitution.

Julia Hosdez

11 Rue Clauzel

We do not believe that a more ugly, insignificant little black thing has ever trod the common path. She has made a meteor-like appearance on the stage of the Palais Royal Théâtre, and we can only ascribe the share of worship she receives to the glamour thrown round a woman by the footlights. But no girl need ever despair in this city, as long as she is not squeamish in bed but will sigh, 'I love you!' to every man, whether he be a handsome youth, fresh from a bath of perfume, or a hoary old sniffer, who abhors soap and water. Julia lives with a poor clerk who earns but a few pounds weekly, but the indigent scribe carefully keeps in the background, while his mistress is earning the wherewithal to buy her unscrupulous Romeo a winter greatcoat.

Alice Howard

37 Avenue d'Iéna

We have to declare with feelings of mingled pride and confusion, that the handsomest whore in Paris at the present time is this Englishwoman, and she has held her position for the last eight or nine years, without having been once forced to abdicate her throne, from which she domineers over all the venal beauties, who bow their heads and proclaim her Queen of Beauty. The Britannic goddess is tall and fair, with languishing blue eyes that can flash fire at times, akin to the lambent light that glitters on a sword-blade. Her nose is of the genuine, tiny, *retroussé*, English style, with palpitating pink nostrils. Her hair is naturally fair, and all the hirsute adornments of her well-knit frame are of the same Saxon tint. But the best part about her we have kept for the *bonne bouche*: although her legs and thighs are fairly good; her skin healthy and her extremities of aristocratic finish; her bearing majestic and disdainful; and her waist so small as could be wished – all these delightful charms are eclipsed by the magnificence of her snowy bosom. For size and shape, these tempting hillocks have never been surpassed, and when she first made her appearance here, they were as handsome as marble. We are not poetically gifted, and therefore cannot sufficiently describe Alice's incomparable bust, but we earnestly implore all admirers of the loveliest part of womanhood to come and see her twin hemi-spheres, and their adorable, rosy, tantalising nipples. Miss Howard is now about twenty-seven years of age, having made her appearance in Paris in 1873, when she had just lost her maidenhead at the age of seventeen. She had run away from her home in London, where she was being respectably brought up, with a gentleman who had taken her to Brussels, and after debauching her, had abandoned his conquest, without leaving the usual consolatory compensation be-hind. She had been a flower girl at the London Philharmonic Theatre or music-hall, before her flight, and we need scarcely say that 'Howard' is merely a *nom de guerre*. But as nearly all her family are still living, we do not feel at liberty to divulge the name of the London tradesman who is her father. The first steps of the lovely girl were fraught with difficulty, as the selfish debauchees of the French capital were contented to reward her cheaply, and trading on her ignorance, enjoyed her youthful charms for the most insignifi-cant wages. But she got 'spoony' on a poor artist, who taught her to go about her business, and pointed out to her the proper haunts to frequent. After a short campaign at Mabille and the Folies Bergères, Alice soon got taken into aristocratic keeping, and since then has found two fine young fellows, who have successively ruined them-selves for her and been forced to leave the country. Whatever she does with the princely sums that have been lavished upon her is a mystery, as she is always hard-up and ever ready to accord an amatory meeting in return for a ten-pound note. Her current expenses are heavy, the maintenance of her private *bijou* residence, carriages and horses, coachmen, footmen, etc., absorbing a tidy sum. Her temper is vile, being rendered so by her inordinate vanity in the first place; and secondly, by a feeling of remorse and shame for the life she leads, that has never been entirely stamped out. This awkward sentiment we have often noticed among unfortunates who hail from the British Isles, and it is one which leads them to drown their persistent regrets in the bottle. She does not take much trouble with the casual companion of her couch, being too proud to stoop to strange caresses, but she likes to be spoilt, petted, lauded up to the skies, and above all enjoys the tender kisses of voluptuous adepts of Sapphic wiles, whether male or female. She speaks French fairly well, with a strong accent, and having found out that a haughty bearing suits her best, holds her small, shapely head like an empress, with her impertinent nose scornfully scouring the sky. She dresses without much taste – although the cheapest toilette looks well on her sculptural frame – and disfigures herself with a senseless display of false jewellery. She has been taking fencing lessons lately, and has been seen at a *salle d'armes*, clad in a lavender jersey tightly stretched over her rich, pointed, pear-shaped breasts. To pass away the long winter evenings she drove herself into an insane love fit, and gushed madly over a big-boned, comic singer at a low music-hall, and would go there night after night, shamelessly bombarding the vulgar, howling wretch with flowers, to the great delight of the sweeps, butcher boys and rag-pickers who formed the audience. She is a good rider, and on horseback, with her tight-fitting habit clinging to her heavily-laden corset, is a most splendid picture. Sometimes she reclines in a two-horse victoria, and then she appears as the true presentment of the frigid Juggernaut whore, crushing the hearts of the besotted votaries at her shrine. Alice is easily accessible, either to visitors direct or by the intermediary negotiations of a procuress, but woe to the nincompoop who should get thoroughly 'mashed' by this cold, unscrupulous siren. We beg to set a board up here, marked 'Dangerous', and our concluding counsel is that the lucky possessor of Alice Howard's body for an hour or a night should enjoy the pleasure to be found in her arms, remunerate her generously and go on his way rejoicing.

Fanny Jackson

3 RUE DE TEHERAN

The debauched girls of our big manufacturing towns generally manage to make their way to Paris, where they find ready bidders for that which they are forced to bestow for nothing on their superiors in the country. This nutbrown damsel is one of our new recruits, and hails from Lyons. At present she is located at the above convenient house, which lets furnished lodgings by the month, week, day or hour. Despite the fact that one or two of her front teeth are a trifle shady in their colour, Fanny is an agreeable coaxer, and will not fail soon to find suitable surroundings for her pleasant frame and laughing face, albeit her features are slightly irregular. In the meanwhile, pending the arrival of the rich keeper, the youthful whore is delighting casual customers, who often return to the charge because the bill is not a heavy one. She trades under an English name, but there is nothing British about her, nor any trace of coyness to prevent her using all her charms like a genuine French, submissive, salacious, gentleman's toy.

Jaeger

MENUS-PLAISIRS THÉÂTRE

The photograph of this intoxicating courtesan is to be found in every Parisian print shop, and she achieves between the sheets a series of nightly triumphs that are much greater than her stage successes. Her luscious body is stout and succulent, although her stature is below the ordinary standard, and her eyes are bright and vivacious. Jaeger is cheap and clean, while her *sanctum sanctorum* is crisp and firm.

Sabine Jamet

92 BOULEVARD MALESHERBES

A young woman with lively eyes, excellent state of bodily health and a supple frame that she keeps in condition by an assiduous study of the art of fencing. She is very expert with the foils, and the agility of her wrist is often sorely tried by slow-blooded rakes, but she triumphantly passes the ordeal. Her soft white hand is very successful just now, as she has not long been initiated in the mysteries of Venus. A courteous, discreet prince is her principal lover. He keeps the pot boiling and is sensible enough to retire into the background when his Sabine is earning a little of the vile metal. But his reward comes afterwards, when his mistress, who is gay and witty, narrates for his benefit her amorous exploits in every detail. Her stories rouse him to fresh life, and our noble, voluntary cuckold is happy. This doughty amazonian wench is short and fair, with plenty of flesh on her bones, a very attractive manner and an engaging face that is full of ever-changing expression.

Janvier

OPÉRA

All the women at the National Academy of Music are venal whores, and to trace their biographies would necessitate a volume devoted to that building alone, which is nothing more than a gigantic bawdy-house. From the apprentice ballet girl, just out of her teens, down to the high-salaried principal songstress, all are to be had for the asking – the payment varying from a supper and a new pair of boots, to hundreds of pounds. We mention this lady because she is an insatiable devotee of lesbian love, and pursues her prey in the corridors of the Opéra like a man. She is short and dark, with a splendid pair of legs and thighs that cause her to be chosen to play pages. She is a very good-looking woman, with a large mouth, the lips of which are of a bright crimson colour, borrowing their feverish warmth from the youthful, unfledged tails she is so fond of chewing.

Jeanny

1 Rue de Maubeuge

This is one of the numerous, cheap, little teasers with which our city abounds, and who do their business deftly, at a figure that places their bodies in the embrace of the most economical libertines. Jeanny is not very pretty, nor very proud, and her only ambition is to content her customers without trying heartlessly to lead them to ruin, as do many of her more fortunate sisters. She is short and rather plump, with auburn hair and good eyes, and her age is about twenty-four.

Berthe Jost

48 Boulevard Haussmann

Although no chicken, this pleasing lady manages to earn sufficient to live in good style, and as she is well educated, and knows how to perform the duties of an affable hostess, is much sought after by a select circle. She is a brunette of medium size, with pale face and dark circles beneath her eyes, caused by constant attacks of that disagreeable malady the 'whites'. She has travelled a good deal, principally in Russia, where she has left many friends. As an actress she has met with some applause, and although her rendering of the part of Madame Lange is sufficiently intelligent, she is seen at her best by her own fireside, when her artful blandishments, rendered still more delicious by the adjuncts of perfume and fine lace-trimmed linen, will delight the eye and vivify the organs of the most worn-out votary of Cupid.

Anna Judic

VARIÉTÉS THÉÂTRE

Most of our readers have seen this charming actress on the stage, where she shines out, eclipsing all the *opéra-bouffe* stars of the present day. She was born in 1850, and was brought up behind the scenes of the Gymnase Théâtre, the manager of which was her uncle. Her sister kept the café next door to the theatre, and her mother was employed at the booking office. Saucy little Mademoiselle Damiens, for that was her maiden name, married M. Judic in 1867, and the couple lived happily together, although in a state of poverty. Several children have been born, but they are not all cognisant of their real fathers' names, for obvious reasons. After vegetating at music-halls, where she was a great favourite, Anna took to the stage, and there, by dint of hard work, succeeded in making her mark. Her dapper little Jewish husband has long ago ceased to be jealous, and contents himself with the office of cashier. He looks after the children, negotiates with managers and superintends dressmakers, while his merry, laughing wife gives way to moneyed offers. All her earnings are put by carefully by the honest pimp, who adores his spouse, and, as we write, their dwelling at 15 Rue de Boulogne will soon be vacant as a handsome villa is being expressly built for them in gorgeous style. She is dark, with a pale complexion and splendid black eyes and hair. Her teeth are regular and white and she takes great care of them. In order to accumulate wealth, she has never spared her sturdy frame, tremendous bosom and monumental backside. Consequently, these charms are rather loose and flabby, and all her dresses are lined inside with stout canvas, so as to keep her big, unruly bubbies in their proper place. Still she is a fine, mellow, juicy comrade in the universal game, and a night with her means money well spent. She is always laughing, with a silvery tone that is peculiar to herself and entrancing to the ear. Her state of health is very good, although the dear creature suffers from constipation that sometimes degenerates into piles. She has some fine jewellery, and a splendid collection of presents from rich admirers in Belgium, Russia and England. In these two latter countries she has been honoured by the caresses of most exalted personages.

Mary Julien

GYMNASE THÉÂTRE

A dark, little, tragic actress, with piercing black orbs, brilliant teeth and aquiline nose. She is a thorough musician, and was educated for the operatic stage, but changing her mind, studied for tragedy and achieved deserved success in leading parts. Her figure is fairly good, and although she has reached the age of thirty-four, she does not look more than twenty-five, as she has been very careful of her charms. She is a perfect lady *en ville*, but a very devil in bed, as her nerves are so highly strung. When in a passion she will break everything she can lay her hands upon; and when on the stage is so engrossed in her part that her comrades often get pinched and slapped in reality, as she is too excitable to make believe. This is a good fault when in a man's arms, so all who approach her may depend upon having their money's worth.

Madeleine Kajerack

11 RUE FORTIN

An impure beauty, who ranks among the well-off whores, having as yet met with no great reverses of fortune. She is a strapping brunette, with blue eyes and a large healthy mouth that sports a hairy wart on the upper lip, while her figure is *svelte* and graceful, being kept within bounds by regular exercise on the back of a thoroughbred hack. Her fortune comes from England, as we are told that Madeleine is well known in London. About a year ago she was always on the move between the two countries, and had adopted the name of 'Warner'. She speaks the Queen's English faultlessly, and gives out that she was born in the tight little island, but we have reason to believe that Denmark is the country where she first saw the light. Her tastes are 'horsey' in the extreme, and she is the only Parisian plaything who drives about in a private hansom. Her dwelling is elegantly furnished, and she gives capital dinners to her friends, both male and female. Of the latter she has an army, for

Madeleine is a confirmed tribade. This venial sin does not prevent her being eagerly sought after by all the lords of creation, who are only too proud to be allowed to let down the flap of their breeches in her laboratory. Her boudoir is a branch office of the Tower of Babel, for her tastes are cosmopolitan, and her lovers are drawn from all parts of the globe – Australia, Russia and Brazil furnishing sturdy morsels to fill her ever-longing, insatiable gap. But her reputation is that of a good-hearted, joyful woman, and to oblige a friend, either male or female, Kajerack would go through fire or urine. Her motto is: 'A short life and a merry one.'

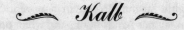

Kalb

COMÉDIE FRANÇAISE THÉÂTRE

A vivacious 'chambermaid', who graduated at the Vaudeville Théâtre. She is very expert in the art of loving enjoyment, and may be recommended as a most cosy partner on a cold night. She is not over tall, but carries herself gracefully, showing off to advantage all her natural charms. Her black hair in wavy curls, her impudent nose and well-shaped mouth merit admiration. Blessed with an evenly-balanced temper and moderate aspirations, she is bound to please all sober rakes.

De Kastillon

50 BOULEVARD DE COURCELLES

Once upon a time there was an old harlot who had two daughters, and she was kept by a gentleman bearing the name we have given above, although we are not certain whether it ought to be written with a 'K' or a 'C'. The sensual old nobleman, when weak and enfeebled on his deathbed, was cajoled into sending for a priest, and bestowed upon his worn-out concubine the honoured title of 'wife'. When the ceremony *in extremis* was accomplished, the gentleman breathed his last, and left Madame de Kastillon and her girls alone in the world. So she made haste to sell her daughters, and the younger, Beatrice, has had the most success. The elder is timid and retiring, and does but little business. Beatrice, however, has dyed her hair, wears a corset that shows her little bubbies out like oranges on a dish, paints her face, and has become a regular incandescent whore. She is now nineteen, and since the age of fifteen, when her menstrual discharge appeared for the first time, has been sold as a virgin at least half a dozen times. A young man about town noticed her handsome appearance two years ago, at the fashionable water-ing-place of Dieppe, and applying to the mother, was quickly presented with a key to the guileless maid's (?) chamber. Towards midnight, with guilty footsteps, he crept into her bed, and after a terrific struggle, succeeded in battering down the rampart of a sham maidenhead that had been built up by means of a leech-bite. Next morning, the weeping *mater familias* made her appearance, and claimed, with much bad language, a fee of about eight hundred pounds sterling for the damage done to her virgin daughter, who was under age. The rich lover was not easily abashed, but went to seek police assistance, and succeeded in getting out of the toils of this harpy. Since then Beatrice has had a baby, and throwing off all reserve, is open to any reasonable offer. She is slight and small, with the sweetest features imaginable, and a fine head of hair. She is too young to feel any fatigue at present, and the slightest touch of the hand, the lips or the virile member, will bring down gushes of thick and creamy essence. When required, the older sister will diffidently join in the sports, and if this should not be enough to satisfy the imagination of the visitor, the old lady will throw off her *robe de chambre* and stimulate the champion by a view of her antiquated charms, or allow herself to be loved in lesbian style by her dirty little brats.

Katinka

58 Rue Pierre Charron

The kingdom of Hungary has produced this scraggy Jewish moll, who has been common property in Paris for the last five or six years. She is uneducated, plain and slim, of an unscrupulous, grasping disposition, and would hardly have been worthwhile mentioning in this list of whores were it not for the fact of a romantic marriage which lifted her off the pavement, where she nightly offered herself for a single gold piece. A nobleman of her own country, not overburdened with ready money, was her constant visitor, but she held a wealthy customer tightly in her toils, and we are sorry to say that this gentleman, who is an Englishman, bestowed his name upon her. The ill-fated union did not last long, and the crash came in November 1882, when the newly-married gentleman applied to the British tribunals – Probate, Divorce and Admiralty Division. Mr Searle appeared for the petitioner, a gentleman of private means, who prayed for a decree to annul his marriage on the ground that at the time it took place the respondent had a husband living. The petitioner met the respondent in Paris, where he chiefly resided. She told him that she was a Jewess, named Katinka Gutman, and had been married in 1873 at Buda-Pest, of which place she was a native, to a person named Weize, but the marriage was void as it had only been celebrated in the Jewish form without being completed by civil contract. She also showed him a paper signed by a Jewish rabbi at Pest declaring her marriage with Weize null and void. Believing this to be the case the petitioner came to London with the lady, and they were married at a registrar's office on the 20th October 1881. They then returned to Paris, but in January they received a communication from Weize, in which he stated that his marriage with the respondent had never been dissolved. The petitioner instituted enquiries, and asked for a decree of nullity. It was proved that by the Hungarian law a Jewish rabbi could not dissolve a marriage, and that the first marriage of the respondent was valid. Weize is still alive, and keeps a coffee-house in Pest. The learned president granted a decree nisi. In spite of this unpleasant affair the released husband remains the keeper of the bigamous harlot, and her noble compatriot is still to the fore. These disclosures made her the fashion for a time, and amateurs who like a thin-legged, fair, flat-bosomed cow, of about twenty-six, may call at the above address without fear of being turned away.

~ *Lucie de Kerne* ~

125 AVENUE DES CHAMPS ELYSÉES

By birth and education a lady, this favoured prostitute has always lain on her back in obedience to the desires of titled lovers with heaps of money. She is fair, but her blonde hair is all her own, and its colour is natural, while her amber, freckled skin has never been sullied by the taint of paints and powders. Her manners are those of a patrician dame, and her only weakness has been a desperate *amour* a few years since with an Italian prince, the pest of Paris, who lived on her till at last she fairly sickened at his continual rapacious demands. She has now cast off her *maquereau*, and devotes her whole attention to the bringing-up of her handsome son, a little boy whom she delights in dressing in fancy costumes. Lucie's frame is hardy, slight and well knit, and when in amorous combat she can hold her own with the sturdiest cavalier; so none had better seek her magnificent couch, unless they are well *furnished* in every way.

~ *Emilie Kessler* ~

41 RUE DE LISBONNE

Alsatia is the birthplace of this quiet, slight, little minx, but our readers must remember that still waters run deep. Her parents were of the Jewish religion, but their daughter only believes in money, and she has always worked hard to get some. Her efforts have not been crowned with success, and although she is now about twenty-four years of age, she has never been fortunate enough to fall across a rich keeper, but has been forced to live from day to day on the varying contributions of indiscriminate debauchery. This life of ups and downs is having a disastrous effect on a pretty little pair of elastic bubbies, the poor girl being inclined as well to poorness of blood. Her features are very regular; her eyes dark blue; the teeth good, and the general appearance most enticing. She is very loving, and is not averse to a rollicking romp with one of her own sex occasionally, but her principal delight is to drop into the arms of an

Englishman. Those big insulars are strong and clean, says Emilie, and they waste no time in flowery arguments, but come to the point at once. This accessible girl is silly and uneducated, faults which luckily are unperceivable in bed, when her neat body and flowing locks of golden hue will be sure to excite desire in the male, especially when he makes the discovery that her tangled bush is as black as night, affording a rare and pleasant contrast.

~ *Louise Kolb* ~
27 RUE DES MATHURINS

Louise is the daughter of a furniture-maker, of a choleric disposition, who put her into a convent in Germany at the early age of ten. Shortly afterwards he took her to London, but the little Parisian *grisette* grew heartily sick of smoke and fog, and at the age of seventeen, escaped from her stern parent, and started in life for herself in the gay capital. She frequented a dramatic school, intending to come out on the stage, but so many ardent lovers besieged the handsome novice, that she threw over all ideas of study, and blossomed into a queen of the *demi-monde*. She was at once successful, and then bitten again by the old fever, appeared at the Renaissance Théâtre in small operatic parts. Her capricious temper soon caused her to tire of the never-varying round of dramatic duty, and she undertook a journey to Russia, where the rich swells of St Petersburg clustered eagerly around her. But she has now settled down in a very elegant apartment, and is ready and willing to accommodate all comers. She is now about twenty-four, and if a man, would be called a jolly good fellow. She is quick-tempered, but bears no malice, and has a strict horror of all female friendships, including the Sapphic ties of which Parisian unfortunates are generally so fond. Her fellow whores do not like her, but the men do, and that is the principal. She can play the piano, and keeps up a sensible conversation, so that her momentary husband is never wearied while bearing her company. She is dark, of ordinary statue, with blue eyes, and is slightly short-sighted. Her nose is straight, her chin full of dimples; the face oval, and the complexion clear. There is a pretty little beauty-spot on the left side of her neck, and she is a most ardent, enticing demirep, always ready to fly into the arms of her favourite. She will be as kind and convenient as the most unabashed, shameless lecher could desire, and will not refuse to give up her secret posterior beauties to be ravished and enjoyed by those who are inclined for pederastic sport.

∽ *Marie Kolb* ∽
AMBIGU THÉÂTRE

A pleasant, little ball of fat, with a snub nose and lascivious eyes. Her bubbies can scarcely be kept down in an ordinary pair of stays, and her hard posteriors, full of health, blush all over at the slightest slap. She appeared on the stage when quite a child, and has been the mistress of a celebrated actor, whom she adored. He got married, and she was forced to accept the homage of promiscuous suitors, whereupon she contrived to please all those who sought repose on her embroidered pillows. No one has a word to say against this merry hussy, who contents her man without demanding any exorbitant emolument. She is gifted with a very nice voice, and is as jolly off the stage as on, which is saying a good deal. A strong fellow, with a *good appetite*, will here find his match, and be squeezed with exuberant signs of joy, between two of the handsomest thighs ever seen on a robust twenty-five-year-old whore.

∽ *Gabrielle Krauss* ∽
OPÉRA

This lady is one of the principal singers of the day, but if her voice was ever to fail, she might earn a livelihood by appearing at fairs as a lovely giantess. She is dark, with strongly-marked features, and of colossal build. All her delightful parts are of massive proportion, her breasts and buttocks being of the largest size and best quality. She was born in Vienna in 1842, and, endowed with the musical gifts, worked hard to attain eminence on the lyric stage, but did not appear at the Opéra till 1875. The *diva* is a fervent Catholic, and like most women who are deeply religious is of a most amorous disposition. But she is far from mercenary, although she knows how to take care of the money she earns in her profession, and her amatory propensities are generally allowed to have full rein when she stumbles across a man who suits her fancy for the moment. Still she is but a weak woman, although physically as strong as a mare, and a polite invitation, accompanied by a bank note, will bring her into the arms of any amateur who likes a lot of hard flesh for his money.

Blanche de Labarre

49B AVENUE D'ANTIN

A clever and designing instrument of pleasure, whose birthplace was the thriving town of Rouen, where she saw the light some twenty-six years ago. Her family was a poor one, and she possesses six or seven sisters and brothers. A red-breeched captain of infantry first caused the moisture of desire to exude from the *nymphae* of Blanche, and she gladly gave up her maidenhead to the robust young officer. After a year's pleasure with him, she dashed off to Paris and took a situation at the big linen-draper's shop at the sign of the Printemps, where she was employed in the corset department. The habit of continually taking off and trying on so many pairs of stays seems to have had an effect on her morals, and made her ever afterwards only too ready to unlace her own, and let the first comer shake her teats and pinch her nipples. She did not long remain in this humble position, but went to live with a young fellow, who may be supposed to have been her first and only love. When he left her some time afterwards to contract a real marriage, she was sorely affected, and ever since has been grave in her manner towards the bollock-danglers of Paris. Since then she has paired off several times, and has never refused a carnal assault of arms with any wealthy wrestler who has cast down a French letter as a challenge to the noble bitch. Blanche has feathered her nest and besides having furnished a very cosy little home, can boast of having scraped from the foreskins of her admirers a neat collection of economical flakes that amount to the sum of two thousand pounds. She manages to make herself very useful to her female acquaintances, and having got into their good graces tries to run away with their lovers. In spite of this intriguing spirit, she is well liked by her fallen sisters, as she is very fond of pushing her head beneath their petticoats and leading them on to Paradise, *via* Lesbos. The crisp clitoris of Henriette de Barras (see page 18), still tingles when she thinks of Blanche's hard and industrious tongue, for these two cows were fast friends once, till pecuniary quarrels drove them far apart. De Labarre dresses well, drives a buggy with her own fair masturbating hands, and manages her cob as cleverly as she does the men who come to her to have a few joyful drops dragged from their enervated tools. She is tall, thin and yellow, with blue eyes, and a growth of long hairs under her pointed chin which she keeps down by constant use of energetic depilatories. Her cleverness in acting upon the weaknesses of the lords of the creation enables her to keep four sensual lovers going at once. They are all friends, and each one thinks that he is the sole occupant of her bed. To sum up: she is simply a sharp, sour-tempered, naturally clever sow, and should only be used like a ripe orange; squeeze out her juice and throw her away, for if you try her again you will soon find your teeth biting into the bitter peel.

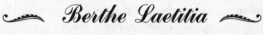

Berthe Laetitia

CHÂTELET THÉÂTRE

A mellow, fat woman, whose age borders upon thirty and who has taken to the stage in order to show her legs to the best advantage. Her dramatic talent is about one degree above zero, but her industry on her soft mattress is something extraordinary. She is short, and her well-rounded form is developed to the utmost, all her bones being covered with firm layers of elastic flesh and her breasts and buttocks being sights to be seen. While on the stage, her bright-brown eyes are continually wandering round the house, as her only ambition is to find a chance bedfellow for the night, when thankful for a brace of napoleons, she will cuddle and kiss him all night. This silly creature has never succeeded in attaching a single generous lover in her chains, but remains the obedient servile whore of the moneyed multitude. Do not be abashed at the lavish display of pearls and diamonds that adorn her bouncing body – they are all false. Her conversation is as babyish as her ways. She is a silly, voluptuous goose, and the only fault about her is that some of her front teeth evidently want renewing.

~ *Amélie Latour* ~

32 AVENUE DE L'OPÉRA

One of the queens of Parisian prostitution when Napoleon the Third was on the throne, this famous whore has no intention of abdicating yet, and her aristocratic fingers cling to the sceptre of royalty and the sceptre of mankind with a grip that tightens more than ever as her charms begin to fade. Her real name is Julia Lieutet, and she was born in the suburbs of Paris, where for years she was a simple laundress. She used to carry home the washing to the customers, who, in return for the clean linen she brought, would often rumple her chemise and petticoats. One day, a dramatic author, charmed by her beauty, assisted her on to the stage, and in small operatic parts she soon became the petted darling of the debauched visitors to the Tuileries. She was a tall, lovely young woman of about twenty-three just before the war, and her lissom frame, deep blue eyes and dyed fair hair made the spectator in the theatre forget that she had no genius, and only a thin, quivering, tinkling, tin-pot voice. Then she was covered in diamonds; now she is worn out, and one of her poor eyes is well nigh sightless. She was, when in her prime, a roaring, tearing whore, and every dish of enjoyment has been well emptied by her. Always fond of her own sex, she has buried her handsome head between the legs of all the women she could seduce, progressing from her waiting-maid till she revelled in the ugly gash of waddling Thérèsa, the famous comic singer. In the early part of her career a child was born to her, and turned out to be a beautiful girl. She ran away with one of her mother's lovers, a young aristocrat in the army, and there was a suppressed scandal that nearly broke the old whore's heart. A few years later, which brings us up to the present day, she fell in love with a young American sharper, who borrowed all her savings and invested them in a swindling company for imitating leather. This was the last straw that demolished Amélie, and now her last vestiges of imperial beauty are in the market at considerably reduced rates. We have mislaid our *Handbook of Latin Quotations*, and therefore cannot work in here the hackneyed *Sic transit*, &c.

The Sisters de Lamothe

9 RUE FORTIN AND 81 RUE DE LA BOETIE

Angèle is the name of one and Rachel is the name of the other. They are very much alike; but Rachel, a year or two the elder, is slightly taller. They are both ignorant and stupid, with big mouths containing good teeth, round moon-like faces, Roman noses, fresh complexions and full, healthy figures. They have been for some few years on the town, and their respective ages now may be reckoned as dangerously near thirty. Rachel is the most tropical whore of the two, not being happy when alone in bed, and frequently sleeping for weeks together with a different man. By gaslight they look extremely attractive, and are really not bad bits of goods for those who want a sharp scientific encounter, and no time wasted in useless philandering. They are assiduous frequenters of the fashionable cafés of the Boulevard each night, and at the approach of winter pack up their bidets for Nice, where they astonish all beholders by their ultra-fashionable get-up and flash bearing. We have given the addresses of the two, and they live within a stone's throw of each other. We do not know which dwelling is Rachel's, or which is Angèle's, but it is not of the slightest consequence to the casual visitor, for if the charming occupant of one apartment is out when he calls, or *otherwise engaged*, he can trot round to the other. The welcome is the same in both places, the attractions are about on a par, and at neither place is anything ever given away.

Thecla de Lancry

'Newly installed at 18 Rue Saint Lazare, on the second floor, and knowing, Sir, that you are a great amateur and *connoisseur* of pretty things, you will be very amiable, Sir, if you will do me the honour and the pleasure to come and visit my very choice collection of statuettes and miniatures.' Such is the circular sent out all over Paris by this indefatigable lady, neatly written in mauve ink on fancy paper, adorned with a coronet. She is nothing more than a *maquerelle*, and the 'collection' is merely the assemblage of cheap whores with complexions too brilliant, waists too small and bubbies too large, who wait patiently between the hours of 2 and 4 p.m. for the advent of the amateur with a member itching for the fray. It is not our intention in this work to depict the manners and customs of the procuresses with which our city abounds, but we are forced to mention this obliging lady, as she does not disdain to have a finger in the pie occasionally, and will be always pleased to *jog* the lazy visitor to her harem, who may like a young woman in front and an old one behind. Thecla is fat, fair and forty, with a greasy skin, and a veritable Niagara of loose flesh when her stays are unlaced. Her real name is Lorsikoff and she was born in Belgium – the peaceful country where so many dainty things come from. She has carried on her lucrative trade for many years under various *aliases*, and has been behind prison bolts and bars once or twice. Her troubles have always arisen from the circumstance that she deals in early delicacies, and can throw into the greedy arms of used-up manhood, the unsullied bodies of mere girls. Even now a telegram sent to her demanding a *primeur* for any hour will enable the amateur to pick and choose between several unfledged lasses. She is expert in all branches of her trade: virginities carefully prepared; floggings conducted with celerity and dispatch in town or country; orgies arranged; groups after the antique tastefully designed and carried out. Pederastic and lesbian clients may rely upon having their orders carefully executed. NB – No money returned. All goods warranted.

～ *Marie de Lannoy* ～

7 RUE DUMONT D'URVILLE

A tall, fair woman, with a most charming set of features forming a blue-eyed baby face that is perfect till she opens her full red lips. Then it will be seen that her teeth are yellow and damaged, and she speaks with a strong lisp. Her age is a mystery, as she has four big sons, one of them being about twenty years of age. He is the eldest, and he writes his mammy's letters, as Marie is without the slightest vestige of education. The second son is the recognised bastard of a Roumanian prince, who has settled a small yearly income upon him. All this interesting family live higgledy-piggledy together, adoring their mamma, and we must not forget the worthy grandfather, who reads the newspapers in the drawing-room, and keeps company with his daughter's lecherous lovers, as they wait their turn to enjoy her remnants of beauty. Her body is well worn, and her poor stomach, burnt by excesses of all kinds and a generation of late suppers, often betrays her, and pretty Marie shoots the feline quadruped in the middle of a meal. Her principal lover, for the last few years, has been an undersized, livid, pox-eaten, Italian gentleman, who has spent his fortune with her. Now he rides about Paris with her sons, and waits patiently till his mistress has a night 'off', and then if she is kind enough to send for him, he fiddles over her for a few minutes, heaves a deep sigh, smashes an ulcer and goes to sleep. She has many ups and downs of fortune within the year, but is always well dressed, and is very fascinating till you get close to her. She has been a paid strumpet since the tender age of fifteen, and the only drawback to her gilded career has been her wonderful fecundity. When the cold weather sets in, she is off to Monaco, where she plays heavily all the winter and generally comes back to Paris with no money. But she always gets some, as she has many rich lovers, who all spoil her. Why they should like this bit of dry skin, who is vulgar and ignorant in the extreme, is one of those things 'no fellow can understand', but human folly is without a limit, as these pages amply show.

Countess de Lansay

Château de Louveciennes

This lady is in the jealous keeping of a Levantine banker, who is one of the richest men in the world. It is not very probable that our readers will be tempted to run after an old American adventuress, with dyed carrotty hair, skinny frame, pointed nose and painted face, but she is none the less worthy of notice in these pages. Her real name is Mrs Jackson, and she has lived for the last twelve years with this old financier, and has succeeded in obtaining complete sway over his senile passions. For her he has bought the Louveciennes estate, where lived the Dubarry whore, formerly mistress of Louis XV, and has spent millions in restoring it to the state it was in when inhabited by the royal pet a hundred years ago. All the vestiges of Dubarry's splendour, furniture, porcelain and decorations have been fished out of the four parts of the earth, and placed back for the glorification of the little naughty slit that rules the world. Mrs Jackson's infatuated lecher gave four thousand pounds sterling for a small marble clock some short time ago, and the Yankee moll can boast of the possession of a service of china, the plates of which are worth at least ten pounds a piece. Amateurs of *bric-à-brac* can now gird up their loins and go down on their knees till their testicles trail on the floor, in order to beg an invitation to this palatial residence on the banks of the Seine. They will find there everything antiquated and out of date, including the loose charms and withered skin of the ugly pampered hostess.

Francine de Laroche

28 RUE TRONCHET

Alas! this address is simply a *maison meublée*; the poor moll has never put by anything, but has always spent freely in every way. She hails from Lyons, where she was born of 'poor, but honest' parents. In 1873 she was servant of all work in a beer-shop, and afterwards in a more elegant café. At that time she was about sixteen, and after sleeping with nearly all the men about town, as she was a lovely young creature, left for Paris, because creditors began to clamour after her sperm-stained tail. Her reckless habits of extravagance prevented her ever furnishing an apartment of her own, but she worked all the hotels of Paris till she became better known than trusted. The *table d'hôte* of the Hôtel Splendide was her happy hunting ground during the Exhibition year of 1878, and acting the demure young widow, she would gracefully play off her charms on the strangers assembled, and whisk them up to her bedroom, when her sweet aperture took in the horny morsel of the yankee who had 'struck ile', and the wrinkled appendage of the pale-faced, High-Church darling, who at home was given to solitary pleasure. Her pranks gave rise to much scandal and as she was continually being pursued by bailiffs who tried in despair to seize her personal effects, the proprietors of the house were obliged to kick her out, and even then she managed to leave owing a pretty little bill. Since then she has rolled about between Paris and Lyons, trying to dodge her creditors and leaving her bits of rags and jewellery in charge of various friends, for fear of seizure. Every year she goes to London, puts up at a swell procuress's and, returning to Paris as penniless as before, boasts of her astounding villa in St John's Wood. She is a great liar, and her ignorance exceeds her vanity. The famous Marquis de Sade was one day mentioned in her presence, and so as to appear as if she knew everything, she burst into the conversation and coolly exclaimed: 'Oh, yes! I know him well – *I dined with him last night.*' Clever scamps have taken advantage of her folly, and as she always boasts of the thousands she possesses, they pretended to believe her, and after having had connection with her, and bent her to their disgusting wills, left her alone in her glory without giving her a penny. She was very intimate for many years with Valentine d'Egbord (see page 61), and the two women used to pass their spare time in biting each other's parts, till they quarrelled in the usual manner about some gamecock or the other. Still she is a remarkably nice piece of pie, and knows how to enjoy a strong man, not yet having lost her taste for the real article. She is a small, dark, natty woman, with only a suspicion of a bosom, and a little, hard backside, with rounded golden buttocks, and a light auburn, curly bush. She has dyed her raven locks to the same tint, affording a happy contrast to the dark sweeping lashes that shade a pair of beautiful light-blue eyes. Under the picturesque cognomen of Neroly she went on the stage at the Menus Plaisirs Théâtre last winter, when in spite of her gorgeous *toilettes*, partly obtained on credit as usual, she was a dire failure, her words passing with difficulty through her white teeth and cherry lips. There are, however, many worse birds fluttering around Paris than this soiled dove, who is a warm, soft, tender little nestler when comes the witching hour.

Mathilde Lasseny

20 RUE BREMONTIER

A gutter wench of Belleville; low, cheeky, and rough; she used to be the idol of the Eldorado Concert-Hall many years ago. Hervé was leader of the band; he wrote her songs, drummed them into her, and turned her up on the piano whenever it suited him. For the last fifteen years she has been richly kept by a Russian prince, who revels in her brutality, viciousness, extravagance and love of brandy. Mathilde cares not for her rich master, but scatters his roubles broadcast, sleeping occasionally with the first counter-jumper, hairdresser or corn-cutter who takes her mad fancy. Indeed, Mathilde says herself that if the prince was to leave her, there is not a man in Paris who would give her a sou to save her from starvation. She has always got her low relations around her draggle-tailed dressing-gown, and she swears and fights with them, but finally makes it up over a bottle, and slips a banknote into their democratic paws, that have never been known to earn an honest penny. If her temperament is not over warm, her imagination is depraved and deranged, and she is celebrated for the leches and whims that she has had, has got, and means to have. She keeps open house, and her dining-room is always full of lords, dukes, swell-mobsmen, third-rate actors, comic singers down on their luck, lousy artists, sculptors out of collar and three-card men on the lookout for a cheap meal. She is continually changing her residence, and has resided in every quarter of Paris in turn. In the Place Vendôme, the neighbours still remember the fire she once had, when dead drunk and clad only in her chemise she insisted upon helping the men at the engine, and pumped away for dear life. Madly eccentric in the choice of her lodgings, of her furniture, and in her tastes and passions, she once had the mania to scour the low halls, in company with Leonide Leblanc, in search of big soldiers, and rumour says that they dried up every drum major of the garrison of Paris. Then she found the money for a theatre which failed, and going to Russia gave way to lesbianism, and stabbed one of her victims in a fit of jealousy. Mathilde does not make the slightest difficulty when her admirers turn her round, and show her how Socrates loved his pupils. This pederastic passion once made her very ill, but she has not given it up, nor any other of her vices either. She is now about thirty-eight, and is a tall, fair woman with large blue eyes that seem to start out of her head, a straight, big nose and a silly look generally. Her walk is that of a big, unwieldy camel, but her careless Bohemian style has great charms for such palates that are *blasé* upon women who still know how to blush, and possess some vestige of womanly grace and shame. Lasseny has a large barrel-organ behind her bed, in the room adjoining, and she makes her maid turn the handle while she is enjoying her *grind* on the big couch, where she has often sprawled out in a drunken fit, flooding the lace-edged sheets with urine and vomiting over her lovers, of whom perhaps she has a brace together, performing the delicious *sandwich* feat, which is practised in the highest circles. Mathilde is mad.

Countess Latischeff

11 RUE DE LA PÉPINIÈRE

The best part of this intelligent little bird of prey is her apartment, which is furnished with the greatest luxury and good taste. A few years ago – let us say six or seven summers, so as not to be too cruel – there lived in Paris a tiny milliner's apprentice, named Léonie Blandin, who was then about seventeen. She emigrated to Russia, and her career in the snowy country is enshrouded in mystery. In 1880 she returned, with a full purse and the high-sounding title we have given above. She began to frequent all the race-meetings round Paris, and being gifted with a plentiful amount of low cunning succeeded in working herself into a good position among the numerous haunters of the Ring. She took care never to say no to members of the press, who in return for a night's pleasure or an hour's masturbation, would sing her praises in their journals. So this imitation Russian lady has succeeded in gathering around her scented petticoats a strong contingent of customers, who pay punctually for the meagre entertainment that Latischeff gives them on her brocaded sofa. She is clever, although seemingly dull and stupid, and once in her hands a man is squeezed dry of all the money he has to spare. She is of middling height, her head poised between a pair of high shoulders and making a great show of her towy hair, which is liberally mixed with false tresses. Her face is small, the nose pointed, and she resorts to artificial colouring. Her figure is nothing out of the common, and she affects a drawling Russian accent when speaking. Her private *money-box* is but slightly covered with hair, and we are told that it requires twenty minutes of careful titillation on the bud of pleasure before condescending to become moistened with the advance symptoms of desire. Being of a lazy, indifferent disposition, she has no friends among other whores and is generally to be found alone. She is short-sighted, and carries a pair of hand-glasses, that give her a very impertinent style. The noble beauty is very well known in all the haunts of pleasure, both by gaslight and daylight, and for that reason had best be avoided by all those who like fresh juicy articles and not dried-up, tough bits of meat that require a deal of *chewing* before they can be digested. She has lately become the avowed mistress of a dirty octogenarian proprietor of a scandalous daily newspaper.

Emilie Laus

11 Rue Greffulhe

She was unknown in Paris a few months ago, but she is bound to become one of the most celebrated whores of the capital. She is a dark, small, Italian woman, of most perfect figure, and a long waist, with a fall in the back that is only seen on a Grecian statue. Her face is refined and melancholic – her almond eyes being full of poetical, languid sweetness – and her mouth is small with sharply-defined, voluptuous lips. Turin is the town which gave her birth, and from the age of fifteen she has worn the fleshings and muslin bandage of the ballet-girl. She came out at Milan, and was soon all the rage, till one admirer, more enthusiastic and richer than the rest, made her a present of a beautifully furnished house, for her and her heirs for ever. She is known on the other side of the Alps as the Princess Lulu, and her supper-parties are the talk of all the fashionable macaroni-chewers of her native land. She next went to Cairo, and after a successful campaign among the sodomites of the Pyramids, returned to Naples, and tried to give up the saltatory profession, but love of her art soon forced her on the boards once more. Her beloved mother died, and Lulu had serious thoughts of retiring to a convent, as her warm, southern, impulsive nature prompts her often to take rash decisions, and she does nothing by halves, as all who have sought her couch can testify. When the ballet *troupe* of La Scala came to Paris last winter, she accompanied them, and reaped golden opinions in her Eastern *pas seul*, when she wriggled her navel in the fashion that she had learnt in Egypt, to the delight of our randy Parisian lechers.

Lavigne

3 RUE TAITBOUT

An auburn darling, whose tresses may be dyed for aught we know, but it matters very little, as she is but an insignificant piece. She is engaging, but not pretty, and her bust is remarkable by the absence of those heavenly hillocks which are the most ravishing ornaments of the female 'form divine'. By profession, an actress; by taste, a whore. She has met with only slight successes on the stage, but she is a wonderful mimic and her imitations of eminent players of the day are carried out to the life. She lives with a boozy, broken-down journalist, who has tried his fortune at everything, from stockbroking to dramatic authorship, but succeeds best, now that he is separated from his lawful wife, in lying in bed drinking *absinthe* and smoking bad cigarettes, while Lavigne goes out to tug at old men's foreskins till her arm aches.

Alice Lavigne

20 BOULEVARD VOLTAIRE

A slight, chestnut, little thing, of modest aspirations, living in a small apartment on the fifth floor, but which boasts of a narrow balcony. She has a little girl, Margot, now about five years old, and she adores the child, who is very pretty. Alice is an expert actress, now at the Palais Royal Théâtre, where she is always applauded. Her speciality on the stage is the undertaking of eccentric servant girls, for we are sorry to say that Lavigne is very ugly. Her mouth is all on one side, her teeth are yellow, her face is pitted with the smallpox, and her figure resembles a pair of tongs that has been twisted out of shape. She has no bosom and no belly, no thighs and no calves, and she is knock-kneed besides. Despite these manifest drawbacks, she finds customers, as there are many lechers who dislike pretty women, and this ungainly, gnarled whore produces the same effect on their used-up system as drinking vinegar, biting a steel pen or sniffing a urinal. Nevertheless, she is a genial, good-hearted young woman, and is ever able to enliven the most dull debauchee by her ready repartee and witty remarks, which are delivered with a voice as harsh as a pig-driver's. Lavigne likes to sleep with a jockey now and then, and she runs after these miniature men with her beady eyes glittering and her nostrils quivering at the perfume of dung and general stable odour that issues from the choked-up pores of their dirty skins. Indeed, her pursuit became so fierce one day, that the imps of the racing lawns grew sick of her advances, and she was absolutely refused by one of the crew, who stated, however, that he would not mind becoming her *rider* for a *canter* and a *gallop* if properly rewarded for the *mount*, which he argued was far from being a pleasant one.

~~ *Léonide Leblanc* ~~

1 RUE D'OFFEMONT

Here are the remains of true beauty and grace, but it is difficult to do justice to such a celebrated whore in the short space to which we are limited in the present work. She has charmed a generation, and in years to come will be almost as celebrated as a Dubarry, or a Nell Gwynne. Every notable rake has passed at least one night in her arms, for a modern Don Juan's catalogue would not be complete unless he could inscribe therein the honour of having 'had' Leonide Leblanc. She was born in December 1846, and when about seventeen was a first-rate actress at a sixth-rate playhouse, sleeping with dirty actors or seedy authors. One of these poor scribes succeeded in getting her engaged at the Variétés, where her beauty began to be remarked, and she gave way to all demands without thinking of money. Her dramatic career was an irregular one. She appeared at several different theatres, but it is only within the last few years, when her intense beauty began to fade, that she gave full attention to the work of the stage. About 1864, she had already gone through several fortunes. She had eaten a pennyworth of fried potatoes with one admirer, and truffles the following week with another; she had broken the bank at Hamburg, and the roulette at Baden had broken her. Upon returning from Germany, she found awaiting her arrival the sinister figure of the man in possession. After being sold up, she took to literature, and published a book that was all about actresses. Her erotic volume was seized by the imperial police; the fair authoress was fined, and became more in demand than ever. In fact, she is a real Bohemian, and is gifted with the genuine power of witty repartee. It is she who, when told that all whores ought to wear their hearts upon their sleeve, replied: 'Yes, that is the reason why the Venus of Milo has no arms!' A member of a noble French family, who when exiled used to live on the banks of the Thames, is her faithful keeper and intermittent lover, and thanks to his *princely* generosity she has been able to indulge all her expensive tastes, which include *bric-à-brac* hunting and love of gambling. Her house is a palace of the *Arabian Nights*, stocked full of rare furniture, priceless pictures and dazzling diamonds. Her motto is: *Quid mihi?* In person she is of medium height, dark, except when her wayward fancy makes her inclined to change the colour of her tresses to a rich auburn, and her cream-coloured skin covers a divinely-shaped body. Her shoulders are rounded and dimpled; her bosom full, without too much exuberance; and her head is poised on a statuesque neck, while her ears are pink and of microscopic size. Her features are small and beautifully shaped, with sleepy languid eyes adorned with long, silken lashes, and her mouth is ever melting into a Sphinx-like smile, showing an array of pearly teeth. Her health is good but she suffers occasionally from severe attacks of colic. Of all the old glories of Napoleon the Third's corrupt court, she is the best preserved relic, and our concluding advice to all real judges of female loveliness is – hasten to enjoy her at once, ere it be too late. You will find her fighting costume adorable. It consists of a black lace chemise, embroidered with floral patterns over both breasts, where the thighs meet, and on each tempting, posterior cheek.

∽ *Marie Lebon* ∽

23 RUE JOUBERT

Vice-president of the Club des Rieuses, and a devil-may-care, one-down-and-t'other-come-on sort of giggling whore. She is an actress, but her true vocation is to administer to the lecherous wants of moneyed manhood. In that line of business she stands at the head of her profession, and her connection is consequently a very large one. Of ordinary height, with a good figure and pouting bubs, which she shows to greater advantage still by wearing stays that throw out her nipples and pinch in her waist. Her complexion is dark, with plenty of hair of her own, while her sound molars, of glistening purity, show that she has never suffered from any serious disorder. Her peculiar lech is difficult to describe. She is pleased to receive the manly instrument in the tight retreat immediately adjoining the real grotto, and allows her captor to pursue his triumphant course, while she draws down her entrancing elixir by means of the gentle friction of her own white hand. This pleasing play she taught to Louise Kolb, and converted her to sodomy, as we had occasion to remark when writing of the latter lady. Here is Marie Lebon's good health, with long life to her – and may she make many more pederastic proselytes before Venus abandons her into the care of Pluto!

∽ *The Sisters Legault* ∽

4 RUE SAINTE CÉCILE

Here are two fair sisters, with golden hair, blue eyes and gold teeth. They are very much alike in appearance and temperament, being rather inclined to be cold and dry when driven to accomplish the real act of enjoyment. However, as they are very jolly and full of fun, they do not languish long for lovers, and their engagement list is generally well filled. Maria is the name of the eldest; she is a shade prettier than her sister Angèle, and has achieved greater successes on the stage, as they are both actresses. They are completely heartless, and therefore do not lose their heads when in the arms of their momentary sweethearts but calmly attend to the technical details of their undertaking. If sufficient offers are made, the hungry customer may strike a bargain for the pair, and be comfortably *sandwiched* between two blonde firm-fleshed beauties, who are about twenty-five years old.

Berthe Legrand

70 Rue des Martyrs

Her impertinent little face, handsome, although devoid of regularity, is well-known to Parisian worshippers of Priapus, and her delicate body, with its cream-laid skin, has been squeezed between the hairy thighs of wealthy suitors for many years. She is an intelligent blonde, with teeth like a terrier, a nose always in the air and a lazy way of bearing her big hips and bottom that acts on the venereal organisation of men like the vapour of cooked meat on the olfactory nerves of a hungry man. As an actress she has always been applauded, but her real triumphs, pecuniary and otherwise, have taken place when, the playhouses being closed, she has doffed her silken chemise in obedience to the impatient commands of duty and desire. She must be now, reckoning by the time we have known her, on the shady side of thirty, and may be heartily recommended as a very juicy and enjoyable morsel for a young Englishman who, fresh from the awkward caresses of the horny-handed whores of his country, wants to see what a French bit of stuff is capable of doing.

Mary Legrand

22 Rue de Constantinople

Mary is the daughter of a photographer of Versailles, and was born in that town in July 1858. At sixteen years of age, her father having bestowed upon her a most liberal education, she was betrothed to an Italian. But she grew to dislike him and, in spite of paternal curses and other disagreeable reproaches, threw her lover over, and herself into the arms of a young cavalry officer. This hero brought off a complete victory, and broke down the barriers of her virgin fortress. The *amour* was discovered, and the embryo warrior packed off to Africa, leaving Mary with the conventional broken heart and damaged reputation. She soon dried her eyes and graciously responded to the advances of a manufacturer of chemicals, who was fearfully jealous. This new escapade having brought the whole town about her ears, Mary thought of emigrating to Paris, especially as she was beginning to have enough of the Othello-like embraces of the dynamite-maker. So she tried to steal away at night, but her latest admirer caught her in the act, and mad with rage emptied over her a whole bottle of his very best oil of vitriol. Luckily, only her clothes were spoilt, and the mother of her insane admirer stepped forward and gave her son thirty brand new banknotes of a thousand francs each to bestow upon his mistress as some slight compensation for the dastardly assault. But he spent the money himself, and the poor girl came to the gayest town in the world and was taken into sumptuous keeping by a youthful viscount who lived with her a year. She was very fond of him, but having caught him playing at the beast-with-two-backs with her dainty little chambermaid, bundled him out without giving him time to wash his parts, and passed into the arms of a wholesale boot-maker. The Knight of St Crispin was very generous and he made her a present of a little villa in the country, which she still possesses. Mary loved him with her whole heart, but he was faithless too and, when she was ill in bed with inflammation of the lungs, would slink out to seek cheap consolation in the embraces of the painted girls who frequent the supper rooms of Paris. Her last love was a young nobleman of Nantes, and she nursed him through a dangerous illness. His family dragged her from his bedside, and drove her away with kicks and cuffs, but that did not prevent her from visiting him on the sly, and coming down from Paris two or three times weekly to console him. We think we have narrated enough to show that Mary is essentially a good woman. She is all heart, and has no vices. Her figure is so good that she is known as 'The Wasp', and the slimness of the waist does not prevent her from having a large bosom, which is as hard as bubbies ought always to be. She has got a fine, plump neck, arms and legs, and is of fair complexion with fine teeth and a proud carriage. Her female friends are all jealous of her, and would be glad to possess such an ardent nature that makes her as hot as a little devil in the arms of her man, as she is incessantly seeking to vary the postures and prolong the pleasures of copulation. She possesses one quality rare among women – whether honest or simple trolls – she only wishes to be faithful to one man, if she could only find one man who would be faithful to her.

~ *Lemercier* ~

176 Rue de Rivoli

A neat, compact, little whore, who started in life most honestly. She was, and is, the wife of an obscure scribe, but poverty drove her on to the stage. Once in the wings, she found that it was impossible to get first-rate parts entrusted to her care, unless she gave up all idea of reserving *her parts* for the quill-driving spouse. So she fell into sin on the managerial broken-springed couch of the Palais Royal Théâtre, and added a fresh stain to the million of spots that dishonour that wonderful piece of upholstery. She became the mistress of the director, and all went much more merrily than many marriage bells sometimes do. Now, she is at the Gymnase, and a long career of hard work, on and off the stage, has somewhat deteriorated her beauty. She used to be a plump, dark-haired, saucy woman, till she tried the Banting system to reduce her figure. She has succeeded in toning down the threatening fat, but her bubbies remain as a sign of what has passed away, albeit they are flabby; very, very flabby. Lemercier is separated from her wretched husband, but has the custody of three handsome children born of their short-lived union. She has light-blue eyes, false teeth, and bites her nails to the quick, but on the stage and in a photograph looks twenty times more pretty than she really is. She always wears fair wigs when acting, and prefers to impersonate the most loving, innocent, self-sacrificing females. In private life, she is simply silly and selfish, but thoroughly proficient in the trade of teasing and pleasing having lived so long with an old, old man, who taught her patience, while wealthy followers taught her the rest.

Leroux

45 RUE LAFAYETTE

An elderly, but none the less fiery old actress, who opens her flood-gates of pleasure at the slightest masculine contact. Her projecting mouth, with a fine row of well-preserved 'ivories', seems pouting forward for a tempting morsel to be placed between the lips, and her thick and dumpy body impatiently quivers, as if eternally wishing for the pressure of a hurried male. She is universally adored, in spite of her age, for her incessant flow of gaiety, and her enemies, having nothing to say against her, whisper that her teeth are false. In company with Julia de Clery (see p. 37), and Marie Lebon (see p. 112) she founded a female club. Les Rieuses (The Merry Women) is the happy title of this lesbian association, entirely composed of Parisian actresses. They hold a monthly dinner, from which all men are excluded, and when the evening meal is done, these naughty lasses pair off and pass the night with their greedy mouths between each other's thighs.

Lesage

7 RUE CONDORCET

About eight years ago this auburn darling was assiduously studying for the stage, accompanied by her snuffy mother, who maintained a strict guard over the maidenhead of her lovely daughter. Lesage is very pretty; she has a yellow skin and a fair set of teeth but her figure is bad. She is tall, and her bosom is flat, but a liberal amount of padding makes up for this defect. She acts at the Vaudeville Théâtre, and thinks a precious deal too much of her talent, which is only of third-rate order. She has always been a little hypocrite, assuming airs of melancholy, and keeping herself very quiet. But she is none the less amusing for all that, and is doing a serious lucrative trade. No one knows her business, and as she keeps steadily on and never tells lies or boasts of the wealth of her lovers, we may suppose that she is putting money away for her old age. She has got a superb baby, and as she takes great care of her bodily health, all lovers of tranquil joys may place themselves between her legs without fear of being obliged to invest afterwards in a box of capsules and a syringe.

Caroline Letessier

AVENUE DE MESSINE

An old woman now, but she was one of the queens of prostitution some fifteen years ago, and when she passes in her carriage, a fearful wreck, we are forced to ask how it is that she could have accumulated the riches she possesses for she is very ugly and has always been so. A pair of watery, motheaten, red-rimmed eyes; a big nose, with gaping nostrils that she has the habit of continually picking and worrying; a bumpy forehead; her skin rough and pimply, cracked by the use of doubtful paint; her face shining with glycerine when at home, and covered an inch thick with red and white at night – such are the ruins of the whore of the Empire, the divine 'Caro'. Her talent in twisting foolish young sparks and salivating, impotent fumblers round her fingers must have been something out of the common as she always had money when all her dirty sisters in the trade were starving. During the Siege of Paris, when a piece of white bread was a rarity, and the poor molls were dying off like rotten sheep, Letessier walked into the shop of a starving jeweller in the Rue de la Paix, and nearly killed him with joy by buying for ready money a set of silver toilette utensils, including the traditional 'jerry' of the same precious metal. She was originally a dark woman, with light-blue eyes; and was one of the first silly creatures who bleached their hair. To her is due the credit of having discovered the stupid extravagance of Russian swells, and when in her prime she used often to journey to St Petersburg. At last her scandalous love of pelf excited so much indignation in the city of nihilism that she was driven out of the country. To obtain her ends she would leave no stone unturned, and has often bought books on the sly to study the subject that most interested her momentary lover. Last year she sold off her collections of lace, pictures, jewels and ancient furniture, and went to live at the above address. This auction, like every other action of her life, was a commercial speculation, as the best goods were not sold, but went to furnish her new abode. From all such cold, calculating, heartless sirens, half-women and half-leeches, good Lord deliver us!

✦ *Marie Lhiabaster* ✦

114 BOULEVARD MALESHERBES

A fine, dark woman, who when young must have been indeed a luscious, juicy morsel. She is now about forty, but only confesses to twenty-eight! No whore had had greater knocking about on the sea of adversity, or had suffered more at the hands of fickle manhood, till about six years ago, when she stumbled across a rich financier. This was a dwarf-like German Jew who, risen from nothing, had rushed into a colossal fortune on the Stock Exchange. The poor Quasimodo-like wretch suffered from disease of the heart and his health was further undermined by his inordinate desire for unnatural pleasure in the voluptuous, velvety mouth of his mistress. He was proprietor of a newspaper, and ruled the money-market for a time, enabling Marie to feather her nest to a pretty tune. The sumptuous mansion she inhabits was bought, paid for and made over to her, and she filled the spacious rooms with priceless works of art and relics of bygone days. A little lower down the street a house was built for her, which she now lets out, and the rents, which are punctually paid, form a snug little income. She had horses and carriages, costly jewellery and lace, and was able to send her little boy – for she is a mother, and a doting one too – to school at Frankfort-on-the-Main. The young fellow is now about sixteen. Her Croesus was not jealous, and so she indulged in youthful lovers on her own account, and several poor gentlemen have been enabled to settle their gambling debts and keep on paying their livery stable bills through the grateful generosity of lecherous Lhiabaster. Being vain, silly and uneducated, the prosperous courtesan had soon quite a small mob of parasites around her, both male and female, and keeping open house, her dwelling became the scene of brilliant *soirées*, where literature, art and finance were represented by their most illustrious chiefs. The hostess, with the raven locks, which were sometimes dyed; dark-brown eyes; pointed chin and white teeth; fine bosom and broad hips, circulated among the groups, growing fat upon the murmured flattery of the Bohemian authors, painters and poets, who, between two compliments, would stuff a handful of cigars into their coat-tail pockets, or else get speechless drunk and vomit behind the rare plants of her conservatory. Invitations to her parties were greatly sought after, and Marie, although she was known as 'Guele de Raie' (Skate's snout), on account of her protruding lips, resembling the jowl of that ugly fish, was the queen of the dense battalion of Paris whores for a short and merry period. But now comes the famous panic on the Bourse of 1882, and the master of the house is reduced to a state of poverty. He pays everybody in full, and starts afresh, but his health has suffered beyond all hope of cure, and obliged to leave his whore, who cares very little for him, dies miserably, alone and uncared for. Her mistress is left with her riches, but all her friends have fled, including the lovers whose creditors she used to pay, and her only consolation is her little boy and the modest affection of a poor cousin, who now wearing a white jacket and cap, helps her cook to prepare the dinner.

Lorentz

26 RUE MONTHOLON

Another goddess of the Thespian temples, who proudly carries about Paris an immense brace of breasts, with dark nipples of a ruby-brown tint. She is short, and her black hair has been chemically treated till a carrotty hue has developed itself. Her expression is very pleasing and her eyes are of a very uncommon greenish-blue tint. All these peculiar colours to be observed united in her portly person form a thrilling *tout ensemble*, and, as she is a most obedient companion for the couch, whom nothing repels, we may confidently press into her service all randy votaries to love.

~ *Blanche Lowe* ~

21 RUE GALILÉE

Such is the name that this new member of Cythera's army has adopted to carry on her war against men's pockets, and she pronounces it 'love'. Never was denomination more fitly bestowed, as she is really a handsome lump of lust. Her little face is irregular, but intelligent and expressive, and although not precisely pretty, possesses an unknown something that charms and pleases all who approach her. She is about nineteen, and but a short year since was still at boarding-school, whence she emerged to cause great jealousy in the hearts of her fellow-unfortunates. She has always been lucky enough to meet rich suitors, and treating them honestly, has had no cause to regret having chosen the lucrative profession of frank and cynical whoredom. Blanche is of a loving disposition; she has no debts, but some very substantial savings, and her establishment, which is carefully tended, is that of a real lady of the fashionable world. Even her wine-cellar is well-filled, and while she looks after all creature comforts, she does not forget to adorn her handsome body, and dresses in sober English style. A rich American merchant is her principal lover, but he is, luckily, seldom in Paris. Mademoiselle Lowe is gay and good-tempered, and no *fête* is complete without her presence, as never having yet had any pecuniary troubles to sour her mind, she is very kind and good-hearted. She loves pictures, and goes round to all the fashionable studios in the hope of gleaning a few canvases to form a little gallery, and the artists receive her with enthusiasm. To sum up, she is a most enchanting darling, and in bed is as caressing and soft as a tiny, fluttering child.

~ *Alice Lody* ~

12 RUE D'EDIMBOURG

When she was about eighteen her parents rushed her on to the stage, where she was held up by the press as an infant prodigy and everybody thought she was a child of fifteen. Lovers of early delicacies pursued her as madly as dogs after a heated bitch, and she was soon crushed beneath the sweating bodies of elderly amateurs with disgusting leches but full purses. This life of debauchery had a bad effect on her health; her growth was stopped, and she lost nearly all her beauty during this hasty use of her undeveloped charms. She is now between twenty-five and thirty, and is a dark-chestnut, slight little double-jointed kitten, who might be taken for eighteen by the uninitiated. Having no flesh on her bones, she will probably look the same for many years to come, if her state of health permits her to go on acting her usual part of *general receiver*. She is still successful in the dramatic profession, and what is better, possesses several devoted and rich 'gentlemen friends'. She has had several miscarriages, and her sufferings have made her rather querulous and inclined to be bad tempered. For money she will do all you may ask her, and when she has cleaned her teeth, and washed herself clean of all stain and pollution, finds comfort and tranquillity in the caresses of her tiny, intelligent little baby daughter. Her real name is Marie Henry. Léonide Leblanc at one time loved this old-fashioned tartlet with Sapphic frenzy, and was never so happy as when her lips were glued to the hairless slit of languishing Lody. She was made very ill by the insatiable succubus, who only quitted her prey by order of a doctor.

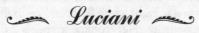

Luciani

Rue Condorcet

About twenty-five, as black as a mulberry and twice as rich and juicy. A thick-lipped mouth with small white teeth, hard white pointed breasts and satin skin. She is always to be heard of at Peters' or the Helder – two well-known night-houses, where she is celebrated for the marvellous affability with which she lends her supple body to the most capricious wishes of her customers, whose names are legion. Everybody knows what a *maquereau* is – a man who lives on women; but here we have a salacious, sucking sow, whose principal income is derived from the presents of tribades. Sometimes she is the priestess, but more often she stretches herself, a willing victim, on the cushions that form the Sapphic altar, and as she twists her lovely form into a bow beneath the influence of the venereal spasm, is a picture to dream of.

~ *Elise Maffioli* ~

45 Rue Joubert

Of Italian descent, this swarthy, angular, bony little piece will be found an incandescent bedfellow. She is generally known as 'Lisette' by a large circle of lovers. For the real struggle she is worth her weight in gold, but will be delighted with a very small sum. Her age is about twenty-three, and amateurs must not be discouraged by a slight moustache upon her pouting upper lip. An exploration in the *low countries* will show that this warm, southern beauty possesses a depth and breadth of flank that is truly remarkable, with a pair of weighty buttocks, and a ripe slit fully covered with bushy adornments.

~ *Berthe Mallet* ~

48 Boulevard Haussmann

A tall, full-flavoured, old, fair bitch; the very woman for a man who likes to wallow in a mass of white flesh, and get lazily led on to the moment of enjoyment. Her commencements in the trade are enshrouded in mystery, but she is generally credited with having started in a bagnio in Lyons, where she was known as Blondinette. By dint of hard work, Berthe became forewoman of the shop, where ready-made love was to be had for cash. If she had remained at this brothel, she might in time have become head-governess and proprietress, but she preferred working on her own bottom, and turned up in Paris. Here she took the name we now know her by, and she stumbled on to a sequence of rich keepers. First came a young artist, and then a banker, and an officer, who when away on service used to pay her liberally and actually believe in her fidelity. She cannot write, although she can manage to read a little. A faithful maid is her secretary, but she was found out by one of her lovers, who, however, forgave her, as Berthe declared that if her hand did not trace the burning protestations of love, her heart dictated them. Blondinette has always felt strong friendship for her sisters in the art, the effect of early habits contracted during the lazy hours in the southern stew. She loves to surround herself with joyful lady friends, and she has done them many a good turn, witness the present position of Reine Romani, whom we present to our readers in her turn. Berthe set her up when she came to Paris, in return for her kindness in clipping her head between her thighs. Madame Mallet could retire now if she cared to, as she has got an income of some forty thousand francs, besides a store of jewels rare. But she loves money, and the trouble of getting it is one of her greatest pleasures. Her large, washed-out blue eyes will light up with a spark of fire when the client, after having been well tickled, licked and kneaded, pays his bill, and departs delighted with Berthe's cunning caresses. The whores of Paris, disgusted at her luck, can find nothing to say against her, except that she started where many of them will finish, and laborious Berthe is to be commended for having carved out for herself a fine, lucrative, independent position, which assures her in her old age plenty of comfort, which is better than consideration or compassion to stumped-out old whores.

Marie Magnier

49 RUE BOISSIÈRE

The father of Marie-Louise-Joséphine Magnier is an old cobbler, who lives in his stall at Boulogne-sur-Mer, while her mother sells fish in the market. He had five daughters, we are told, but the lady whose biography we trace is the only one who has succeeded in becoming sufficiently notorious to merit our attention. Marie started in life as an artificial flower maker, and came to Paris to learn her trade, which she did with a vengeance, becoming very expert in the art of arranging a *rose bud* or *twisting a stem* till it stood triumphantly *erect*. In 1865, she took to studying for the stage, and three years afterwards appeared on the boards of minor theatres and casinos, till after a short campaign at the Palais Royal and Vaude-ville, she has anchored at the Gymnase, having become an expert exponent of genteel comedy. Her *amours* have been as numerous as the stars, and she has tried all kinds of physical emotion. Firstly she got thoroughly mashed by the young actor who is now married to Elluini (see page 63), and then she formed a luscious lesbian *liaison* with Grandville (see page 71). Now she is the toy of an old ducal dotard, who has installed her in a little villa, but this connection does not prevent her from enjoying the robust attacks of a clever comrade of her theatre. She is a tall, fair woman, of striking appearance, and her age must be about forty. The best part about her is her well-poised head and neck; her face is full of expression; her eyes are blue; and her mouth, which is large, is well filled with dazzling white teeth. A hairy wart disfigures this pretty visage, and her lank body has nothing to attract the lovers of sculptural form, as her bosom is flat, her waist square and wooden, and her hands and feet bony and large. Still she is successful, as she is endowed with matchless impudence, and her vanity is overbearing. The passion of gambling reigns supreme in her effervescent brain, and after her duties on the stage are done, she steals away to one of the clandestine gambling-houses with which Paris abounds. She is also an assiduous frequenter of horse-races, as her doddering old protector possesses some of the champions of the turf, and there she is the observed of all observers, by reason of her insane toilettes and mad exclamations. A few months back she complained that she had been robbed of her jewels, among which was a necklace formerly belonging to the wife of the imbecile aristocrat who lives with her, but it was afterwards discovered that mad Marie had plundered herself, to excite pity in the hearts of some of her most pressing creditors. Magnier is a mother, having three or four brats, who are in charge of the Boulogne boot-mender. One of her sisters has appeared on the stage with but little success. Another one acts as her servant, prepares her bath and bidet, and now and then allows her husband to sleep with Marie and herself – all three in the same bed.

Marguerite

VARIÉTÉS THÉÂTRE

Or more familiarly 'Margot'. We have never heard her called by any other name. She is a jolly and agreeable woman, and although only entrusted with little parts, is very fond of her profession, and is always exact at rehearsal. She is about twenty-four, and is tall, tolerably well-formed, with a saucy face and chestnut hair, usually covered on the stage with a blonde wig. She blithely answers the call of all admirers with money, and has no regular keeper. In the daytime she passes her time at a *maquerelle*'s, and at night is ready to sup with any spectator who deigns to wait for her at the stage door. Marguerite is singularly docile in the amorous combat, and is only too glad to do all that is asked of her, from playing a tune on Adam's flute to dancing the *can-can* naked on the supper-table.

Berthe Mariani

18 Rue de la Chaussée d'Antin

Many old Parisian whores go into the curiosity trade when their own curiosities are beginning to get worn out. Berthe, now a full-blown matron, is one of these, and we may counsel a visit to her shop, which is well stocked with porcelain, statues, pictures and works of art. This lady is very intelligent, and her conversation is most interesting and witty. She has written for some of the minor journals, thus proving her to have received a good education, and after a long chat, should the visitor require a little amorous dalliance, he will find the lady greatly pleased to conduct him into the cosy little parlour behind the shop and shake him and kiss him till he reaches the end of his tether.

Louise Marie

14b Rue Jadin

This antiquated charmer, being married to an accommodating husband who is never in the way, calls herself as above, and keeps her surname out of the common mouth. Her age is uncertain, and only such who care for old women will run after this slight, dyed-blonde witch, with thin lips, skinny bust and painted face. She has been well educated, is a good musician, can sing well, and was formerly a ballet-dancer. She has amassed considerable wealth, and now and then levies a tax on an old admirer. There is a very handsome daughter of hers at school in England, and the old harlot is undecided at present whether to throw her into the circulation, or 'make a lady of her'. Her dwelling is sumptuously furnished, and she possesses a priceless collection of original drawings by great masters. Now and then she takes a fancy to a young fellow, and rewards him for his arduous labour in her yawning chasm with an original Eisen or Wouvermans, much to the stupefaction of the robust fancy-men, who prefer hard cash.

⟶ *Alice Marot* ⟵

4 RUE DE MARIGNAN

This sprightly, fair, little whore has been very lucky. After a more than usually chequered career upon the boards of provincial theatres, she came to Paris, and at the Palais Royal Théâtre enlarged the circle of her lovers. Her fellow-workers in the army of Cupid swore that she spoilt the trade, as she tumbled on to her back at all hours of the day and night for any little bit of gold or silver that the good gentlemen crossed her hand with. But she had her mother to keep, and a blonde little rascal of a boy. The son and heir of the founder of the gambling halls of Monaco took her to live with him some two or three years ago, and the wily courtesan has succeeded in getting the upper hand of him. By the exercise of her nimble fingers and warm mouth she is drawing him daily of health, brains and money, putting by all she can for her old age. She is singularly ignorant, and her continual mistakes in conversation have given her a reputation worthy of Mrs Ramsbottom. She has a neat figure, is of medium height and dresses quietly and well. Her face is very pleasing, although there is a dangerous, rapacious, look in her deep-blue eyes. In early life she was married to a bricklayer, who still hangs after her, and she has to silence him by continual gifts of money. Latterly, her lover wished to buy her a ten-thousand-pound house, and the husband's power-of-attorney had to be bought for four hundred sovereigns. Her teeth are none of the whitest, and although she wants for nothing, friends from the theatre are always accommodated *gratis*, for the sake of old times.

∼ *Félicie Marmier* ∼
49 RUE CAUMARTIN

She must have been a fine creature in her day, but she is now about forty-five, and shows no signs of giving up her trade. Félicie has a fine figure, with enormous loose bubbies, and her dark, expressive, bold features still appear attractive behind a spotted veil. She can neither read nor write, but plenty of men like old women, and for such she is a hard-working treasure. Nothing comes amiss to her, and we have been told that she handles in a masterly manner a cunning shaft of smooth ivory, with which she figures a pederastic attack during the act of copulation. Let all those who require a *postilion* rush to her at once, when they will find to their surprise that she always wears short socks, like a man, as her legs are round, smooth and shapely.

∼ *Marsy* ∼
COMÉDIE FRANÇAISE

We blush to state that the subject of the present sketch – whose real name is Brochard – is a real virgin, and her mother, who never leaves her, means to keep her intact, if not unsullied, till after her *début* on the stage. At the time we write, she has not yet appeared as an actress, although engaged at the above playhouse. Madame Brochard, the careful maternal parent, is a fine blonde woman of about thirty-eight, with blooming bubbies and pearly teeth. She lives with a fashionable contributor to periodical literature of an erotic kind, and his friends declare that she is killing the clever young writer by the voluptuous, but too frequent caresses of her mellow mouth. Her daughter is now twenty, and is as fair as her mother, extremely handsome, tall and well built, with a rich golden complexion and skin like a ripe russet apple. Every day this delicious pair is to be seen driving in the Bois de Boulogne, and we advise all longing lechers to pursue the mother, hunt her down, and, after enjoying her matured charms, to put their names down for a turn at the girl when the proper time comes. If the chicken turns out as randy a whore as the old hen, there are still some happy days in store for Parisian rakes with long purses and a *lingam* to match.

Jeanne de Marsy
19 AVENUE DE VILLIERS

Should this mercenary charmer be out when you call, there is no need to turn away while yet hungry, as the house is inhabited by several other ladies in the same line of business, as our readers may see upon turning over these pages. Marsy is twenty-four, and looks like a cameo, being thin and having aristocratic features. Her hair is dyed fair and worn well off her noble forehead, but her bones are nicely covered with soft, warm, firm flesh. Directly she runs into a little ready cash she gets haughty, and goes about with her nose in the air, refusing to look at anybody and treating her poorer sisters in the trade like the dirt under her feet. Hence she is universally disliked, and hunts after her *meat* alone and unaided. Jeanne is indefatigable in bed, and amateurs will find her clean, and her shapely body well tended and perfumed. She is very reckless in monetary matters and is always in debt, having been seized and sold up quite recently. Her real name is Jeanne Huart, but she does not like to be reminded of her plebeian denomination and extraction.

Marie Martin
COMÉDIE FRANÇAISE THÉÂTRE

A fine, dark, Spanish-looking, matronly woman, with semi-globes like a Dutch sailor's wench, and a pair of hips and a monumental backside that would make a Turk go off like a bottle of ginger-beer on a hot day. She is full of *love juice*, and brims over with lecherous desire, so that her principal keeper cannot manage to satisfy her. He is the representative in Paris of the most powerful journal in the world, and gives his massive mistress as much money as she wants. She has been his toy for the last three years, and before then had been through many hands, both male and female, as Marie likes the lingering love of Lesbos. One of her strongest attachments was formed with the mistress of a bathhouse, and the two salacious nymphs used to disport in warm, perfumed water for hours together, much to the delight of the male attendants of the establishment, who nearly ruined themselves in the indiscriminate purchase of gimlets. Madam Martin's dark skin has a peculiar odour of its own, which all the scents and washing in the world cannot overcome, and this negress-like smell causes her to be greatly sought after by old sniffers who can no longer plant their *standards in the field of pleasure*, but are forced to content themselves with groping caresses and lengthened suction.

~~~ *Léontine Massin* ~~~

We have delayed going to press for some time in order to find the dwelling of this vivacious little actress, but she is erratic in her movements, and changes her abode so often in order to dodge her numerous creditors that all our efforts have been in vain. Nevertheless, she will always be found by a *maquerelle*, and as her charges are modest, no better means can be found for a first interview. Plump Léontine-Louise Massin is now about thirty, and she was born of middle-class parents, who had her respectably brought up at boarding-school. At the age of thirteen she ran away with a lover as far as Constantinople, where she appeared at a music-hall, and even at that age she became expert in the diversions of debauchery, the Turks teaching her the pleasure to be found on *both sides of the medal*. A year or two afterwards she returned to Paris with a small sum of money, and made her *début* at the Folies-Marigny Théâtre. She soon became the centre of a select fornicative circle, and went to the Palais Royal and Gymnase, always finding plenty of rich lovers. But she was ever a silly little goose, and used to spend all she earned on the fancy-man of the moment. She is particularly fond of actors and horse-dealers, gentlemen who generally succeed in getting their 'greens' for nothing, and therefore has always been poor. She fell madly in love with a stage lover, and lived *for* him and *with* him for some two or three years in a little village near Paris, till starvation drove her into the arms of a lusty prince, who will one day be king of the greatest country in the world – the country that rules the sea. Her quondam lover has just died in a mad house, and Léontine has fared very little better. She was engaged at the Ambigo Théâtre, and stole the heart of her manager after a determined fight with Lina Monte. Her keeper spent all the takings with her, and things going wrong, strove to end his life by means of a pistol-shot. He recovered, nursed by the grateful actress, and winding up his affairs retired to Monaco. It was there that last year poor Léontine had a paralytic stroke, but she has now happily recovered, and no one would think that she has ever been ill. Considering that she has been a prostitute for twenty years, she is wonderfully well preserved, and still shows vestiges of great beauty. She is short, plump and chubby, with lovely blue eyes, fair hair and complexion and splendid pulpy lips that she is always biting and licking with her rosy tongue. Her panting bosom has always been renowned for its splendid size, but it has lost its pristine firmness. Her legs and bottom are small and thin, but her manner is so agreeable and she is so good-hearted that a night or two may be comfortably spent in her arms, and the amateur may find her just as enjoyable as many a younger woman. The poor thing laments her reckless extravagance, now that it is too late. She created the part of Zola's heroine, Nana, and her life resembles greatly that of the imaginary courtesan. Like her, she will die alone, poor and uncared for, after charming a generation of seekers after erotic excitement and having handled the tarriwags of rich and poor, from the prince to the peasant. Some slight symptoms of old syphilitic combats have manifested themselves lately, but there is no danger, and Massin, to drown dull care, has resorted to the cheering glass.

Thérèse Meilhan

5 Rue Caroline

Her mother used to keep a hotel in a street leading out of the Champs Elysées, and she gave her daughter a first-class education. Mingling with the visitors of all nations who frequented the establishment, little Thérèse soon began to speak English fluently, and her vicious disposition and tropical temperament led her to wander in and out of the numbered rooms, and travellers from all climes tickled her girlish concern. In one day she can boast of having been masturbated by a Chinaman, her breasts sucked by a Spaniard, while an Italian ejaculated in her tiny hands and an old English clergyman tasted her early seed. Her maidenhead was soon destroyed, at her own desire, by a youthful blood relation, and she would try the powers of all the boys in the neighbourhood, who used to pass round the word and bring their comrades to satisfy this baby Messalina. Her mother had no time to look after her, but when she caught her in suspicious play, used to lock her in her room, whereupon Thérèse would utilise these moments of enforced quiet by playing with herself in front of a looking-glass. Her health soon suffered, and having been in full blast at the age of thirteen, it will not surprise anyone to hear that although now about twenty, she is entirely exhausted, and only excessive and unnatural experiments can produce a fitful emission. She was a pupil of the Conservatoire for some years, but successive illnesses, brought on by her wilful lust, prevented her appearing on the public stage. A young actor, married to an old woman, fell in love with her, and the two carried on a mad intrigue, which ended in the comedian's spouse obtaining a judicial separation. He now lives with her entirely, and has taken her to London with him, where he has appeared at the side of Sarah Bernhardt, and with her to second him gives a few select performances in the drawing-rooms of the nobility and gentry. Her beauty may be described as of the washed-out sort. She is small made, fair, with milky skin and large, wondering blue eyes.

Nina Melcy

GYMNASE THÉÂTRE

The favoured whore of a member of the British Parliament, who, instead of attending to his legislative duties, is nearly always in Paris, chained to his charmer's odoriferous tail. Melcy is a tall beauty of twenty-eight summers, and is a very intelligent woman, albeit a mediocre actress. She is thin and fair, with nice teeth, a big nose and enormous feet and hands. Rumour says that she is a very agreeable partner in the game of love, and when crushed beneath a man is 'all over the shop', possessing a serpentine wriggle and a nipping power of contraction that acts on the most flabby instrument. She also adores her own sex, but only when there is an important debate in the House.

Louise Meret

11 Rue Miromesnil

As fair as a corn-stalk and nearly as thin. Her hands and feet are enormous, but her features are pleasing, and lovers of tall women will rush to her apartment. This lady, now in her zenith at the age of twenty-five, is exceedingly tender and winning, and conducts herself in a most respectable manner. She is very well off, having some wealthy lovers who keep in the background but who lavish their money on her so freely that she is able to maintain a stable of the finest carriages and horses in Paris, and dress at the first milliners. She carries her tasty toilettes remarkably well, and when she takes a man in her long arms, lets him have his bellyful but makes him pay for his whistle all the same.

Violette Merschoff

75 Rue de Chaillot

A rank harlot, who is celebrated through her long connection with the late, but not lamented, Duke of Brunswick. This eccentric nobleman used to bend her to his most crapulous caprices, and together they used to dabble in human excrements. This amiable and dirty whore is now over forty, dark, but dyed fair, with a figure like a deal board, a large upturned nose, affording a full view of her cavernous nostrils, and a tremendous gash across her face, which does duty for a mouth. D'Arcourt (see page 15) claims to be descended from the Brunswick family, and she refused to dine with Violette, proudly saying that she would not sit down to table with *her grandfather's mistress!*

Blanche Méry

44 Rue Lafayette

This dark, podgy, Jewish maiden used to be at the Bouffes Théâtre, and she has now migrated to the Palais Royal. Her dramatic talent is small indeed, but her fornicative genius is beyond question. She must be now about twenty-seven, and has had a child by a dramatic critic. She left the stage to live with him, but as he abandoned her, has returned to the footlights, and is disengaged for the present. She suffers greatly from tumours, and wearies would-be lovers with lengthy dissertations on the state of her dear little ovaries. Her belly is enormous, jutting out in front of her like Southport Pier.

Milly Meyer

Nouveautés Théâtre

A miniature woman, with a delightful irregular face and a most winning manner. She is a comic actress of *opéra-bouffe*, possessing an agreeable reedy voice. Her real name is Emilie Mayer, and she is one of the chosen people. She first came out at a low music-hall, and when discovered by an intelligent theatrical manager, was still in possession of her virginity. Jeanne Granier (see page 71), with whom she used to play, took her about 'on the loose', but the tiny Israelitish maiden refused all offers of enjoyment till she found an admirer who bought her a substantial stock of furniture, and leased an apartment to put her into as well. Her age is about twenty-one, and her hair is black, but she generally acts with blonde tresses. She has got a little baby, whose father is a fat Jew with a wife and family of his own, and pretty, intelligent Milly is a good mother and a sweet lecherous darling into the bargain.

∼ *Marthe Miette* ∼
47 AVENUE DES CHAMPS ELYSÉES

She possesses many points of resemblance to Alice Marot (see p. 126), as she also has a little boy and a clever mother who keeps in the background and looks after the housekeeping while her girl trafficks with her charms. Marseilles can boast of having given birth to this charmer, who is really a beautiful woman. She is dark, with a straight handsome nose, large mouth, and magnificent black hair and eyebrows. Her frame is perfection, of fine sturdy make, with a most prominent and magnificent pair of large breasts, which are placed rather low. Her temperament is warm and sensual, and she possesses the gift of contenting several lovers in one day without fatigue. This southern beauty has never been in love, and her experience of men has been of a most bitter kind. She started in life as an artist's model, and was violated by a sculptor when about sixteen. She gave birth to a son, and ever since has lived upon the passions of all those who desired her, without having a spark of feeling for any. She possesses little or no intelligence, except when in bed, and her conversation is wearisome in the extreme. For ten years she played small parts at the Palais Royal Théâtre, but her hard head refused to take in the slightest elements of dramatic tuition, and after having paid her a few francs weekly to appear as a servant girl, bring on letters and open doors, the management was obliged to beg her to leave. No other playhouse cared to engage her, and not being able to advertise her charms in public, her banking account has suffered, and she has been obliged to give up her carriage and pair. But she is a splendid animal for the delights of sex, and may be safely recommended for a luscious night's amusement.

‿ 'Mika' ‿

37 AVENUE KLEBER

Camille Burth is her true name, but she is better known as above. She is the type of a female gambler, and the passion for play has dried up her womb and caused her to care not a jot for copulation. She is short and dark, with a well-furnished body and a busy, bustling manner. Her black hair is cropped as short as a boy's, and she sometimes wears a complete peruke of golden hair. Her general behaviour is that of a vulgar cow, and she is mostly to be found in the society of Marie de Lannoy (see page 102), chattering of her 'luck', and disputing in a shrill voice about abstruse problems of play.

‿ Jenny Mills ‿

CAFÉ-CONCERT DES AMBASSADEURS

A slight, little scrap of a woman, with tolerably well-formed limbs, who succeeds in amusing the Parisians every summer at the above-mentioned music-hall, where performances are held in the open air. Jenny is an English girl, about twenty odd years of age, and her towy hair, small, winning eyes, saucy screech and indecent jig-dancing combine to attract a few lechers, whose offerings, added to her salary, just keep the pot boiling. Miss Mills has travelled about considerably in her time, and has learnt sufficient to enable her to be as clever at her trade as the most accomplished French whore. St Petersburg swells have enjoyed her thin body, and she has sung comic songs to the rich Jews of Vienna, while even the phlegmatic Dutch merchants of Amsterdam and Rotterdam have wheezed and coughed over her for hours, according to their usual custom. She is lively, vivacious, and also salacious, and is always ready to put her tongue down the throat of a fellow-countryman.

∼ 'Miss' ∼
65 Rue Prony

Andrée de Cléry is the name of this appetising young woman of pleasure, but she is known as above on account of her fancied resemblance to an English beauty. Whether she resembles the maids of merry England or not, is a matter of taste and opinion, but nevertheless she is extremely pretty. Her features are handsome, harmonious and pleasing; she has large, sparkling brown eyes; a small and delicate nose; cherry lips, and fine teeth. The figure is tall, and sufficiently plump, and she looks and behaves like a lady. About twenty-six summers have passed lightly over her head, and she has just returned from Russia. She has always been the pet of rich men, but of late the receipts have fallen off, and the juicy darling has had to put down her brougham and trot about on foot. Her intelligence is not of the first order, as she has squandered her gains on her toilet, but that is all the better for our amateurs, who can now treat themselves to an hour or two in her sweet company for a comparatively small stake. In the nocturnal *tête-à-tête*, she will be found to be a hard-working, kissable wench, and her only fault is a certain sallowness of the skin, as she suffers from occasional attacks of inflammation of the intestines. De Cléry has been 'gay' for the last ten or eleven years.

∼ Mirecourt ∼
Palais Royal Théâtre

A stout, fair, flabby matron of unbridled passions. She is very cheap, and is, like most French whores, very fond of licking the genital organs of any woman who will pander to her Sapphic taste.

Elise de Moncy

9 Rue Saint Lazare

An insignificant little brunette, who methodically goes through the usual performance for the smallest gratuity. We mention her in these pages because she belongs to the epistolary class of venal females. Every morning, after her marketing is done, and her bit of cag-mag bought for the morning meal, Elise may be seen seated in a café, poring over the directory; she pesters perfect strangers with letters, informing them that she has something to communicate, and will be at home from two till six. If a man is fool enough to go, he will find the Moncy spider in a dressing-gown of doubtful purity and stinking like a pole-cat of cheap perfumery. Without further ado, she plunges her hand into his breeches, and the trick is done.

Berthe Monget

17 Rue Chaptal

This lady is a chubby actress of medium statue, fair and oily, who graces the Vaudeville stage with her pleasant figure. She is twenty-seven years old, and although having no pretensions to beauty is still a very enjoyable creature, without an atom of vice about her. Her chief lover is a country squire, who is not over-burdened with brains, so that it is easy for her to evade his vigilance when sought after by a casual lover.

Hélène Monnier

Vaudeville Théâtre

'Titine', as she is called by her friends, has been an actress from her childhood, and it can be said of her that she never had a maiden-head, having been introduced to the *raw material* when scarcely in the teens. She has been to London, where her talents were greatly appreciated, and she is now verging upon thirty. She is small, dark, thin, and rather dry where she ought to be moist. Her nose is pointed, and her manner is sharp and decisive. But she is a very good creature, and full of witty chatter.

Céline Montaland

COMÉDIE FRANÇAISE THÉÂTRE

As fat as a quail, as white as marble, and very nearly as firm as ever, with raven black hair. Such is the present condition of this actress who, now about forty-two years of age, has been on the stage since the early age of five. Rarely have we seen a more beautiful woman; all her charms are massive and superb, but her features are small and exquisitely shaped, and her hands and feet are exquisitely tiny. Her ears are rather large, but she hides her only defect by drawing her black hair, worn in two plain bands, right across the top of them. Her fortune, which is a snug one, was drawn from the pockets of the courtiers of the Tuileries, and it is currently reported that the late emperor often forgot the cares of state between her sculptural thighs. She has two boys, who are brought up most respectably. In order to keep her home pure from all scandal, Celine rents an apartment in a so-called 'family hotel', not a hundred miles from the Avenue Friedland, and it is there that favoured lovers are occasionally allowed to taste her sweet body. These confidential orgies take place in the daytime, as Celine is very proud of her beauty, and goes to bed early. Every day she takes an anal injection of tepid water, and ascribes to this practice the preservation of her lily-white complexion and smooth skin. Lately, as age creeps on, Celine has delighted in the Tantalus touches of a tribade's tongue, and she has debauched many young women, forcing them to kiss her numerous charms till the desired end be at last attained. She is a very clever woman, and is a great favourite in Russia.

～ *Betsy Monthozon* ～

21 RUE BEAUJON

In a tastefully decorated apartment on the fifth floor lives this ladylike courtesan, and on the fourth storey is the snug abode of Marie Robert, who is fully described further on. Betsy is about twenty-three years of age; fair, thin, and of medium height, with blue, staring, hysterical eyes; nice teeth; fine skin, innocent of contamination by paints or powders, but generally freckled by the kisses of Phoebus. Her lovely mount is plentifully shadowed with dark-brown curls, but her bubbies are slight. She is the daughter of Belgian parents of independent means, who have been domiciled in Paris since 1873, and we do not feel at liberty to divulge their true name. Monthozon ran away from school in 1878, and lived for about eighteen months with a gentleman who gambled his fortune away and left her. She then threw in her lot with the descendant of a general, famed in French history, till mutual misunderstandings drove her into the arms of a sworn broker of the Bourse, with whom she is now living. She is tolerably faithful to him, and he is very much in love with his dainty concubine, who can play the piano, sing, and do the honours of his house like a real lady, thanks to her substantial education. She is very fond of Cupid's sport, as her nature is warm and impulsive. Her nerves often prove stronger than her natural prudence, and she has been known to take up a knife to a gentleman who had been 'chaffing' her. Her friends accuse her of trying the effect of Sappho's favourite pastime with her neighbour, Marie Robert, but she swears the contrary, and declares that she likes that style of promoting pleasure well enough when passively submitting to the tender touches of a delicate gentleman's mouth and tongue.

～ *Noémie Muller* ～

21 RUE DE NAPLES

A vivacious, pretty little fair pet, who after graduating as a prowling whore at the skating rink, where she could be picked up and made use of for a gold piece, took to the stage, and now figures in the back row of choristers at the Variétés. She is short and slight, with twinkling beady eyes, and her age must be dangerously near twenty-five. She is very vulgar, and her early training makes her a pliant instrument in the hands of an expert debauchee. No keeper is in the way to frustrate her plans of promiscuous pleasure, and she is accessible to all at any hour of the day or night.

Ernestine Munié

19B AVENUE D'ANTIN

A fine girl, of medium height, straight and well made, with bold features, good eyes, black hair, white, clean teeth and a very small waist. She has not been 'out' more than three or four years, and is yet fresher than most of the Paris prostitutes. She was destined for the stage, but has not yet reached the boards, as her light-hearted, merry disposition will not allow her to submit to the trammels of tuition. She is a most amusing companion, and is very fond of essaying all kinds of postures when on a couch with a lusty fellow who likes true pleasure and wastes no time in preliminary touches.

Lina Munte

GYMNASE THÉÂTRE

One of the lean kine, and the thinnest woman in Paris after the divine Sarah Bernhardt. Her age is about twenty-five, and she is as black as a coal, with livid circles beneath her eyes, and a sarcastic smile ever hovering round her thin lips. She used to live with a provincial tenor singer, who was madly jealous of her, and before he departed to fulfil an engagement in the provinces led her to a cemetery and made her swear fidelity on a tombstone. Lina soon perjured herself, as she became the mistress of the proprietor of the Ambigu Théâtre, till she was supplanted by blonde little Massin, whose life we describe on page 129. At this playhouse she created the part of wicked Virginie, in the drama of *Drink*, and used to shine out in the washhouse scene, when she deluged her stage rival with water. She caused the death of the actress who used to receive the douche nightly by changing the bucket of tepid water for one of icy-cold temperature, and that while the poor lady was suffering from her monthly derangement. At least, so says the widowed husband, who is now seeking consolation on the flat chest of Marie Magnier. He is the 'clever comrade' to whom we alluded when speaking of that latter enchantress.

Elsie Murton

81 Avenue Montaigne

England has sent us this dark, pale beauty, who owns to twenty-five summers, and possesses all the vices of a downright moll, as she tipples on the sly, and enjoys a young girl as much as a man. She now lives quietly enough with a young and rich commercial gentleman, but a substantial gift will draw her from her retirement. She is small and plump, with fine teeth, and when in the act of enjoyment, likes to be as nude as when she was born, and forces her playfellow to adopt the same absence of costume.

Marie de Nauroy

14 Rue Keppler

The daughter of a worthy pair of humble *concierges*, who now that their daughter has elevated herself to an exalted position in the world of prostitution are excessively proud that their offspring is a harlot. Marie is a few years over thirty, and she can boast that she has ruined two or three rich fools. With her spoils she has bought a fine house, and keeps a splendid establishment. One of this siren's victims is an American, who spent his stock of dollars freely with her, and when she kicked him out, without broaching a keg, announced his intention of returning to his native land and making another fortune to come back and lay at her feet. In the meantime, she is fattening on a wealthy Cuban, who is exceedingly jealous, but she finds means to make him ridiculous in the society of a number of little, well-dressed youths, who are always dangling after her with their members in a state of erection and their fingers smelling of Nauroy's scent and glutinous discharge. The fascinating creature is a martyr to chlorosis, as her extraordinary complexion, like diaphanous porcelain, amply shows. She is the lovely Queen of Anaemia and Fairy of the Whites. Her face and figure are most pleasing, and when quite young she must have been of dazzling beauty. Her conversation and bearing proclaim her to have been carefully educated, and her society is charming in every way. She possesses vast property near Saint-Malo, and for those who like pale, fragile, blonde beauty, will be found worthy of a visit. Her terms are high, as it will be seen she is in no immediate want of money, but is too fond of saving up all she can to throw a chance away.

Nesta Needham

17 RUE DUMONT D'URVILLE

When this English courtesan was married to the gentleman whose name she has dragged through the mire, she candidly confessed that she merely chose him so as to get a start in life. Although well brought up and coming from a good old family, she early professed a taste for debauchery, and when she had broken the heart of the poor wretch who had placed the ring on her finger, coolly left him, and coming to the Continent, offered her spare charms to the highest bidder. She is the type of a thin English lady, with ordinary features, long nose, nice eyes and a fair set of teeth. Her body is lank, and there is a complete absence of those pleasant promontories that form feminine beauty. She looks something like a man in woman's clothes, and is familiarly known as 'Bobbie' in consequence. When she crossed the channel, about three or four years ago, she had just come of age, and she ambitiously made up her mind to become the most flaring whore in Europe. Her *début* in the prostitutive arena was fraught with difficulty, and she led a busy Bohemian life, offering her lean frame at reduced rates to the broken-down gamblers of such pleasure places as Spa, Ostend and Boulogne-sur-Mer. She seems to have sailed into smooth water just now, as she has been taken into comfortable keeping by a rich Englishman, living in Paris. He is a notable cuckold, whose spouse ran away with her several children and a lusty horse-dealer, so he now consoles himself in Bobbie's bed. He does not care much for her, merely maintaining her as a kind of doll companion, whose duty is to be dressed up expensively, sit by his side in his phaeton and hold her tongue. My lady is fond of a dram, and drinks her lover, who is a three-bottle man, under the table.

Christine Nilsson

HÔTEL CONTINENTAL

It is interesting to trace a successful career to its origin. Madame Nilsson is the daughter of very poor parents, natives of an obscure village in Sweden. They were jacks of all trades, and very musical. Christine had at a very early age to do for herself, and was patronised by the owner of a ferry, who took country folks across one of the many lakes about the hamlet. She was started by him as an infant prodigy, and her singing and violin playing drew customers from a rival boat. When she was big enough, she tramped with her father and mother from fair to fair. It must not be supposed from this that she was on the low level of the women and children who tramp through Kent in the hop season. Poverty is not so degrading in Sweden as in Great Britain, and as hospitality is a universal good quality among the peasants of Scandinavia, Christine was not exposed to degrading hardships in her roving childhood. It was at a country fair that an influential Swedish gentleman discovered her musical genius, hearing her sing to violin accompaniment which she played herself. She was now fourteen, and her discoverer obtained for her the protection of the King and Queen of Sweden, opened to her the academy of Stockholm, and when she was fit to go to Paris, sent her there to study under Wartel. She was ungrateful to her benefactor, who caused her triumph in Paris through getting hold of the Emperor and the Empress of the French, by means of the King of Sweden and Dr Evans the dentist. Of her subsequent triumphs all over the world it is needless for us to speak, nor is it necessary to sketch the personal appearance of a lady whose portrait is always cropping up in illustrated papers, to the despair of purchasers of that silly kind of literature, who must be heartily sick of her face, which alternates with that of Madame Patti, an ugly old statesman with big collars and a portly royal personage who is always laying foundation stones on the front page. We are bound in justice to state that no man's name has ever been coupled with this charming singer's, but she is known to be one of the most industrious tribades that ever grew moist at the sight of a fresh young girl. Her husband's madness and consequent death was caused by his terrific jealousy of the wife's victims. She would turn in disgust from his legitimate caresses to fly to perverted lesbian diversions, and only cared for his approaches in the same manner. The strongly marked, steel-blue pupils of her eyes proclaim the sensual longings of a strong imagination allied to a cold temperament, but it is a pity that her desires should run in such a channel.

∽ *Andrée de Nolda* ∽

67 RUE JOUFFROY

A superb and fleshy bitch, who inhabits one of the finest villas in her quarter, furnished with every modern stylish luxury. Andrée is a jolly woman with no foolish affectation about her, and all the money and surroundings she possesses have been freely offered to her, for she is too good-hearted and improvident ever to have torn the banknotes from the men, as many whores do. The bulk of her fortune comes from the liberality of a mad South American gentleman, to whom she was frankly unfaithful. She would throw herself down to all his friends, and he frequently used to find her in bed with strange men. He would then adjourn to the *cabinet de toilette*, and wait till she was done, as his 'great love' excused her wrongs. She once was thin, but she is now as fat as bacon, at the age of twenty-four. She is fair, with lovely blue eyes; healthy, clean skin; good teeth, and a bosom, rich, firm, and abundant. She never wears stays, and she loves to show her tremendous, white, heaving globes, surmounted by rich strawberry nipples. She was originally a governess, and during an engagement in England, became affianced to the son of the house where she lived, but she soon gave up her marriage projects, and came back to Paris to lead a free life. The young Englishman is still waiting for her. Her education is perfect; she speaks English well, and possesses all the proper diplomas of her original calling. There is something masculine in her manner and temperament, as Andrée adores adventure, and she often scours the low haunts of our city to pick up fledglings for her private diversions, which are those of a thorough tribade. She is a great glutton when it comes to sucking the slits of her female friends, and she sends letters and flowers to any creature whose clitoris she covets. She is fond of her home, of horses and domestic pets, besides a little gambling now and then. She is at present in love with a young member of the Stock Exchange, but he gives her nothing in return for her hospitality, dinners and presents, except strong proofs of manly vigour. Her name, 'Nolda', is an anagram, being that of her first lover read backwards.

Gabrielle Nordez

NOUVEAUTÉS THÉÂTRE

A young, dark, slight actress, who is very expert in the numerous ramifications of her art. She shows at her best when the visitor chooses her ruby mouth as the altar on which to pour out his sacrifice to Venus, and is exceedingly smart when the *blasé* amateur implores her to take up a bunch of twigs, adorned with coloured ribbons, and gaily whip him along the road to pleasure. The most aristocratic bums have bled with joy beneath her tingling birch, and her lectures to her grown-up pupils are fantastic and eloquent in the extreme, although unfortunately delivered in her native language.

Norette

NOUVEAUTÉS THÉÂTRE

This is another of the insignificant actress whores who crowd the Parisian stage and are always ready to receive the spectators after their performance. This lump of lechery is a third-rate *opéra-bouffe* girl; small, dark and thin; with a pointed nose, and an agreeable bearing. She has been passed from hand to hand for the last five or six years, so that she thoroughly knows her business, and is expert in the art of pleasing a man of slightly salacious tastes.

Oceana

48 RUE DE CHAILLOT

Daughter of a numerous family of circus riders and acrobats, who are all well known in Germany. This queen of the sawdust was married to a performer in her own sphere, but the sober enjoyment of the marriage bed palled on her depraved spirit and she came to Paris, where she soon became the rage. It was the correct thing a few years since to have slept at least one night with Oceana, and if want of money or lack of manly power precluded that joyous debauch, our rakes would wait upon her at the circus and present her with big bouquets. In public, she capers on a 'slack wire', juggling meanwhile with empty bottles; in private, she is a demon with a man, and can reduce the sturdiest rogue to a placid nonentity in one night, so great are her powers of spermatic absorption. One gentleman, madly in love with her, gained an attack of paralysis as a reward for his excessive attempts to satisfy her, and the terrible misfortune overcame him while in her very arms. Since then she has preyed upon the general public, and all who have had the pleasure of gloating over her naked body proclaim it to be one of nature's sculptural masterpieces. Her face is the worst part about her, as her features are of the masculine order, and her teeth are rather yellow. She is fair and well knit, of medium height, and all her charms are in proportion, with no undue allowance in any one part. Her husband has died of drink and grief since she abandoned him, and of late Oceana's vogue has been somewhat on the wane. She tried the stage in order to gratify her ambition for show and applause, but she was a dire failure, and so has returned to the ring, where she is as much at home in the saddle as on the tightrope. A female acrobat throwing double somersaults without a rag to cover her, is a splendid sight for a worn-out rake, whose passions require a strong fillip, therefore in her private capacity she is doing extremely well, and should not be overlooked by libertines with money. Strange to say, in spite of repeated diurnal purifications, her private parts always emit a very strong effluvium. This idiosyncrasy is objected to by many fastidious rakes, while there are plenty who are very fond of this peculiar marine savour and odour.

Georgette Ollivier

7 RUE MEYERBEER

A gorgeous creature of mature age, who, virtually retired from active warfare, lives in a fine apartment near the Opéra. She is dark, well built, with substantial thighs and proportionate beauty of bust. Her skin is white and smooth, her black eyes brilliant and saucy, and her splendid head of hair has been chemically treated till it has attained the auburn hue seen in Titian's pictures. She was formerly in the company of the Palais Royal Théâtre, and was never without rich lovers. To enjoy the charm of her society, and have the pleasure of listening quietly to the most dulcet voice that ever issued from a whore's ripe lips, an introduction is necessary, and the monetary gift, which must be a heavy one, should be discreetly offered, as this juicy goddess, although disposed to dispense her gravy in return for gold, is excessively susceptible and sensitive.

Countess Oratcheska

12 RUE AUBER

Some men find their powers of enjoyment doubled and trebled when they hold in their arms a woman of aristocratic birth, even should their wanton be one of the most unblushing whores in existence. To those whose snobbery follows them between the sheets, the address of the above facile dame will be a treat indeed, but we advise them to be careful, as this authentic Polish countess is celebrated for sending away her admirers with the seeds of inflammatory gonorrhoea every time that she forgets to take an injection of cold water after copulation. She is a handsome bitch of about thirty, and the crack between her thighs is a fiery furnace, always demanding fresh fuel, and burning with fiercer heat every time it is *poked*. Being well educated, of good family and pleasing address, she does not want for customers; but money is of no use to her, as she squanders it all on dress, and notwithstanding that she has sold her charms freely for the last three years, is still living in furnished apartments. Her monthly bill at milliners and dressmakers amounts to about four hundred pounds sterling, thus precluding all ideas of economising enough to buy furniture. Her mind is warped by excessive erotic desires, and she remains a silly goose. She is tall and good-looking, but only tolerably plump, and her hair is of the chestnut hue, dyed fair. Her nervous temperament causes her to be always blinking one eye. She is very lascivious and very dear, but being, as we have said, a real countess, she gets heaps of rich lovers to follow in her train, while prettier, younger and cheaper harlots are starving in the streets of Paris.

∽ *Marguerite Parrot* ∽

25 AVENUE D'ANTIN

This lustful little whore ran away from her native town, Chantilly, where her parents still live, at the early age of nineteen. Her father had married a second time, and her stepmother behaved very badly to both Marguerite and her sister, who also took an early opportunity of escaping, but she has lived respectably with one lover only, and so drops out of our pages. When Marguerite left her home she was a perfect virgin, and had had no experience of anything but a little solitary pleasure. She remembered that a rich young nobleman had flirted with her and given her his address in Paris some few months before, so she called upon him one fine morning, much to his surprise, as he had already forgotten the fresh country lass whose blushing cheeks he had kissed and whose sprouting bubbies he had pressed under the trees at Chantilly. He respected her maidenhead for a whole fortnight, but at last succumbed to temptation and made her a woman. The young couple led a happy life during four short years of unlimited copulation, till he left her, and she then went boldly out upon the town. She is now about thirty, and has gained sufficient experience and cunning to enable her to keep three lovers going at once, without counting promiscuous sacrifices to Priapus. Madame Parrot is short, fair and plump, with merry blue eyes, and a continual flow of wit, accompanied by incessant outbursts of rippling laughter. She is a good musician, and is always singing scraps of popular songs and torturing her piano. In the act of fornication she is rather cold, and her absence of moisture is a sad drawback when the genuine article is required. Being, however, a good-hearted, genial woman, her society is much sought after, and her shortcomings in bed are forgotten on that account.

Cora Pearl

6 RUE CRISTOPHE COLOMB

One of the most celebrated whores of her time. She has charmed a generation of votaries to Venus, and still goes on undaunted. Her real name is simply Emma Crutch, and she hails from Portsmouth in Great Britain. She was a servant girl, and some twenty odd years ago might have been picked up by the first comer at the defunct Argyle. She made a flying visit to Paris with a lover, and achieved such success in our city that she has remained here ever since. The French language was soon learnt, and Cora, as she called herself, became the reigning harlot of Paris. A member of the imperial family was her lover for many years. He took her to the Opéra on his arm, but they were refused admission. This did not prevent him from going yachting with her in the summer on a government ship. No supper party was complete without her society, and she was once served up naked, with a sprinkling of parsley, upon an enormous dish borne by four men. Her lovely body was modelled by a famous sculptor, and the result exhibited at the Salon. In 1866, she came out at the Bouffes Théâtre, essaying the part of Cupid, but although her costume was studded with diamonds even to her shoe buckles, she showed no talent, and was promptly hissed off the stage by the republican students, and never faced the glare of the footlights again. An accomplished horsewoman, her stables were as handsome as her apartments. She never thought of counting her money, and gold ran through her fingers like water. The sale of the luxurious appointments of her villa occupied several days some few years ago, and the only relics saved from the wreck were her toilette utensils, which are all of solid silver, from her jugs and basins down to the *vase de nuit*. A foolish young fellow shot himself in her presence, and she was ordered out of the country for a few years. Now she is poor, almost friendless, and up to her neck in debt, but she has not lost her merry disposition. No woman was ever so really good-hearted and generous when she had money, and none of her old lovers ever speak of her except in terms of praise. Her features are not pleasing; her hair is dyed fair, but her teeth are magnificent and healthy; and her skin is of dazzling milky whiteness. When undressed, she is a picture, and her flesh is yet hard and cool, although she is quite forty now. She has never omitted using cold water, and is continually drenching her frame with an enormous sponge. To these ablutions and healthy exercise on horseback, we may ascribe the marvellous preservation of her bodily beauty. Every man of any note for the last fifteen years has passed a few hours with Cora, and time flies quickly in her company. Her motto is: *Parcere subjectis et debellare superbos*. There is a great lack of all ceremony about her, and she never took a penny from any man unless he cared to offer it. She is a jolly good fellow, and consequently will die in poverty and misery, as all unselfish people do, whether respectable men and women or only simple-minded whores, like poor old Emma Crutch, who after sleeping in black satin sheets embroidered with the arms of the Empire, now sheds tears of joy when an amateur slips a banknote in her hand.

Countess Pegère

4 Rue Lapérouse

This is the black lady to whom we have already alluded (see page 83). She is a handsome negress from the French colonies, and comes of a well-known noble family. There were three daughters, each well educated, and each possessing a marriage portion of about four thousand pounds. One married a swindler, who soon ate up her dowry, another is still single and the third is the dusky wench we are now writing about. She married a nobleman, whose name she bears and who, when he had squandered her money, left her to go on the town. She is now about twenty-five years of age, slight, well-made, as black as night and as hot as fire. Her teeth are dazzling white, and her manners and conversation are ladylike and charming.

THE PRETTY WOMEN OF PARIS 151

Clarisse Pélletier

5 RUE LORD BYRON

A frank and genial whore, who carries on her trade without disguise and glories in her shame. She is about four and twenty; short; plump; with nice, dark eyes, and sweeping eyelashes that shine out with renewed lustre as her raven locks are dyed fair. She comes from the south and is very well made, having small, hard, pointed breasts which must meet with the approval of all *connoisseurs* of a jolly, devil-may-care disposition. The warm place at her side in bed is never without a wealthy occupier.

Perrine

75 RUE D'ABBEVILLE

A tall, pretty, fair woman, of about twenty-six years of age, with a glorious pair of warm bubbies. She graces the music-hall stage with her presence, but only for the purposes of prostitution, as she has but a piping, shrill little voice. She is very lecherous and gets drunk very often when waiting at a *maquerelle*'s for a gentleman to come and choose her for the pastime of an hour.

Suzanne Pic

ODÉON THÉÂTRE

Like her biblical namesake, Suzanne is always pestered by lecherous old goats, but she prefers young men. She is a middling actress, but a first-class whore. She has just turned twenty, and having been seriously ill, is rather thin, but she will soon fill out, and her short, fair, wizened little body come back to its former plump proportions.

～ *Piccolo* ～

48 RUE GODOT DE MAUROI

A most fascinating wench of the gypsy type, round as a tub, with swarthy skin, a magnificent set of teeth, splendid eyes and a wealth of strong black hair that curls all over her forehead and forms merry little whiskers. Her real name is Camille Wagner, and she is the daughter of a beer-shop keeper. She was seduced when in her teens, and one of her earliest lovers, if not the first, was an old banker, still alive, and to whom she goes whenever she is hard-up. After unlimited fornication all over Paris, she went to live with a Belgian dramatic author, who pitchforked her on to the stage, of which she is a distinguished ornament. She has assiduously cultivated the art of singing, and is now greatly applauded at the Nouveautés Théâtre. Her apartment is well fitted, and she possesses a monster bed that was expressly constructed for one of her keepers, a Spanish swell nearly seven feet tall. She is an adorable mimic, is very quick witted, and rough and ready in her manner. Not over clean in her ways, she always has a multitude of little dogs careering after her clouts, and she adores a lesbian bout, or a spree round the Latin quarter, when she gets roaring drunk. She possesses a little house in the country, and it was there that she lately gave evidence of courage, which those of her friends who knew her best would not have credited her with. Returning to the villa at Nogent-sur-Marne, after the theatre, just as she had put her lights out and retired to rest, she heard a loud scream for help coming from the direction of the garden. Instantly out of bed, without even putting on any other garment, Piccolo seized a revolver and rushed down the staircase, where she found herself in the presence of six rough-looking men. As they advanced to seize hold of her, Piccolo pointed the revolver at the group and fired off one chamber, which so scared the men that they all took flight. Four out of the number effected their escape, but two of them were held by Piccolo and the gardener, the man who had given the alarm which aroused the artist; and they succeeded in holding them till assistance came. The revolver shot had been heard by several neighbours, as well as by a sergeant of police, so that help was almost instantly at hand, and the two men were soon safely lodged in custody.

Blanche Pierson

VAUDEVILLE THÉÂTRE

This lovely, blonde Creole woman was born in the French colonies in 1843, and is still a most enjoyable companion on the couch. Her mother shrewdly guessed that her budding beauty would fetch her a fortune, and she made her an actress, never leaving her till, like Diogenes, she had found an honest man. She sold her to a banker, who gambled away his money and died in Switzerland of a broken heart. Since then Blanche has always had rich keepers, and has become a first-rate actress besides. She can paint fairly, collects old furniture and possesses a luxurious villa near Dieppe. She was once very fat, but Banting's system has reduced her to normal proportions. Her hair is golden, her eyes blue, her little nose is a saucy, pointed one, and she has a most winning smile, when she shows a row of white teeth. She is of medium statue, and her rich bosom is perfection itself.

Princess Pignatelli

RUE CHALGRIN

Marie-Gaetana Pignatelli, Princess of Cerchiara, heiress to her father's title by right of primogeniture and therefore Princess of the Papal Empire, Patrician of Rome and Grandee of Spain of the First-Class, was born in Naples on the 16th November 1850, of the late Fabricio Pignatelli, Prince of Cerchiara, and Rose Capomazga, widow and second wife of the Duke of Regnia, ambassador of Naples at Saint Petersburg. We cannot resist giving our readers the proof that here is a real, live princess, who, having quarrelled with her relations, is taking singing lessons and has gone on the stage at a low music-hall in order to shame her aristocratic connections. She is a little, short-sighted, dark lady, very stout and very excitable. Her sister, Emmanuela Pignatelli, was born at Naples, on the 15th October 1852, and is also a posthumous child. Emmanuela married Count Nicolas Potocki, a Polish nobleman, in London, in the year

1870, and lives in a newly erected palatial mansion in Paris. She is known to be a furious disciple of Sappho, so we see that unbridled lust is hereditary in the family. Marie is also married, having been united in June 1876 to a French gentleman, but by right of primogeniture, according to Italian law, she keeps her title. She is separated from her husband, whose name we shall keep secret, and she has the custody of two fine children. She is very fond of jewellery, and possessing a handsome income, is enabled to gratify her taste for big diamonds and big men. Strong rakes without much money are hereby informed that the princess is far from being exclusive in her choice of lovers and takes nothing from sturdy fellows who know their business when bedtime comes.

Blanche Querette

DEJAZET THÉÂTRE

This bundle of opulent charms has been a very wretched actress for some years, and she is now about twenty-seven. Russia has been honoured by a visit, but she has invested the earnings of indefatigable prostitution in the purchase of the above little theatre. Her fancy-man is the manager, but he is on the verge of bankruptcy. Blanche possesses the largest pair of bubbies at present destined for the common use in Paris and she would be a perfect beauty if her legs were a little longer. She is very stout; dark, with small features, tiny hands and feet, and a most affable manner, but being very short and having a tremendous bust, her aspect is comical indeed. But she is a most lascivious dumpling, and every bit of her fleshy frame is deserving of worship.

Rachel

54 RUE BLANCHE

She is not pretty, but she is well made; dark, even to swarthiness; of medium stature, and only nineteen. She is now living with a lusty old fellow, who tickled her till she left school for him about a twelvemonth ago. She is now seeking for a young lover to entertain her on those nights when the elderly lecher lets her repose in peace, as he cannot always satisfy her newly awakened passions, and she does not like sleeping alone. At the same time she is fond of money, and will do all in her power to earn a few gold pieces.

Maria Rawson

3 RUE MOLLIEN

A nineteen year-old Belgian girl, who is very good company, but does not care for the caresses of male or female. We think of the two she prefers the latter. She is tall, and her hair is dyed fair; she has very little bosom; sleepy, languid, brown eyes and a fine set of teeth. She bites her nails, rolls about Paris disgusted with the world, and seems entirely *blaseé* already.

Jane Ray

11 AVENUE DE LA GRANDE ARMÉE

As yellow as a guinea and quite as flat, although she drags up her skinny dugs and pads her corset till she looks as if she really possessed a fine bust. She was a milliner's apprentice, and used to eke out her small wages by an assiduous frequentation of the Mabille Garden, where she used often to earn a napoleon from some decrepit amateur, fond of budding novices. At last, she got into keeping with a rich old nobleman, who soon afterwards died. His son, nearly dumb and stone deaf, inherited his father's colossal fortune, and his mistress as well, for he now lives with ugly Jane. He leaves her plenty of liberty, of which she is not slow to avail herself. She is dark, with fine black eyes, and she has a little child.

∼ *Raymonde* ∼

72 BOULEVARD HAUSSMANN

The women of the South of France are generally dark, but here we have a curiosity in the shape of a blonde beauty from Bordeaux, where golden tresses are most uncommon. Her real name is Marie Lafon, and her mother kept a hotel, till Offenbach spied out her daughter and brought her out at the Bouffes Théâtre in 1868, when she was only eighteen; the old lady sold off her business, and has lived ever since on the charms of her erratic offspring. Raymonde has knocked about considerably. She went to Egypt just after the war and married a handsome Jew tenor, from whom she was soon separated. She was in London with a French troupe a few years ago, and there caught the pox, which she has succeeded in eradicating. At present, Raymonde is a blonde, plump creature, with splendid teeth and a most engaging manner. Her bosom is very rich and well shaped, though her breasts, being very large, make her look shorter than she really is. Of Bohemian disposition, she does not care for money, and likes going out to balls and theatres with some young fellow to whom she has taken a fancy. Still she does not intend to be made a fool of, and as one old lecher was trying to enjoy her body 'on the cheap', she procured some cow-itch and sprinkled it inside his hat. He never called on her again, and now always pays a harlot's bill like a gentleman.

∼ *Geneviève Razili* ∼

31 RUE SAINT GEORGES

A genuine Parisian lass, and worthy of notice as she is very little known, disliking casual lovers. She was born at Belleville in 1861, and was apprenticed to the feather trade. In 1879 she was seduced by a so-called banker – in reality a usurer, and dabbler in shady transactions. With this man she lived for one year and had a child by him, that is since dead. He got married, only visiting her occasionally thereafter; she was obliged, in order to avoid starvation, to throw herself into the arms of the highest bidder. She gradually progressed in her career, and now is the joyful companion of a select circle of sober and rich rakes. She is well made, extremely dark, with thick, meeting bushy eyebrows, good teeth and an imperceptible moustache. She does not mean to have any more children, and takes an injection of hot water every time a male inundates her womb with the prolific liquor. It is only within the last year that she thoroughly enjoys and appreciates the approach of the manly weapon, and the once cold, coy maid has blossomed into a volcanic whore. All Sapphic play, and the disgusting caresses common to French girls of her class, she holds in horror, and only cares to be thoroughly and repeatedly served. To a healthy man, with clean tastes and vigorous powers of enjoyment, she will be indeed a *rara avis*.

Suzanne Reichemberg

COMÉDIE FRANÇAISE THÉÂTRE

A short, fair, double-jointed, odd little piece, who is no taller than a good-sized umbrella, and very little thicker. She is the granddaughter of Suzanne Brohan, a famous actress, who had her educated for the stage; at the age of fifteen, she took the first prize at the Conservatoire, in the year 1868. She soon afterwards appeared at the above theatre, of which she has become one of the brightest ornaments. Being bred in the wings of a theatre, and cunningly tutored, she only allowed her friends and professors the small change of Cupid's coin, resolving to allow no one but a solid and rich lover to penetrate into the recesses of her virgin grotto. Her line of conduct was successful, as she stumbled on to the descendant of a rich Irish family domiciled for years in France, and he bought her a house worth eight thousand pounds. In return, he got a maidenhead that must have been a mere cobweb, worn away as it was by repeated tongueing and fingering. He had a child by his babyish mistress, and she is now open to discreet offers, accompanied by proper inducements, at her private address, 21 Villa Said.

Gabrielle Réjane

45 RUE BRÉMONTIER

Her true denomination is Charlotte Réju and she is the daughter of
a modest check-taker at the old Ambigu Théâtre. She popped into
the world in 1856, and her young life was passed in misery between
her mother, who, no better than she should be, used to take in work
from a manufactory of pocket-books, and a poor aunt, who is an
ugly old maid, a virtuous bonnet builder. Gabrielle was always a
dirty-nosed, draggle-tailed little slut, who succeeded in obtaining a
second prize, in 1874, at the Conservatoire. She then was engaged
at the Vaudeville, where she now acts, and is celebrated for her
talent of mimicry. She has had more lovers than she can remember,
and is now tightly stuck to a young fellow whose family have made
their fortune in the paper-hanging trade. He gave her the princely
villa where she now lives, and upstairs, in a garret, is the humble old
maid who still goes to work every day at a milliner's. Réjane is far
from being pretty, but she has a kind of saucy charm about her that
pleases many. She is thin and dark, with a crooked mouth, plain
features, irregular teeth and plenty of hair of a chestnut hue. Her
health is bad, in consequence of early indulgence in the art of love,
and she is familiar with the sports of Sappho. She is not at all faithful
to her keeper, and nothing comes amiss to her, as she will never
refuse a pederastic challenge. In short, she is a shameless, intelligent,
entertaining little monkey, who manages to please both male and
female adorers.

Hedwige Reymond

13 AVENUE DE LA GRANDE ARMÉE

A bouncing, big, meaty, Austrian damsel, about twenty-five years of
age. She is fair, with large blue eyes, black, bushy eyebrows and
tremendous, hard, plump bubbies and posterior. She was employed
in a pastry-cook's shop in Vienna and lived with her parents, till she
was seduced by a French commercial gentleman, who took her to

Paris, where she lived with him for three or four years. He left her for a tiny French girl, who Hedwige sought out and fought, nearly killing her rival. She has lately dropped the name of her lover, Reymond, and is better known by her Germanic trademark, Hedwige Borrman. She speaks French with a strong accent, and is a very good-hearted whore, although a little too reserved in bed for Parisian tastes. This is, however, a venial fault, and one which unfortunately will soon rub off.

De Ribeaucourt

81 Boulevard Malesherbes

This once fascinating actress is dangerously near fifty and is kept by an old married man. She has long since retired from the stage, and delights in salacious struggles with mere boys, whom she tenderly initiates into the deepest and dirtiest mysteries of the art of lechery. Fifteen years ago she was divinely handsome, being naturally fair and stout, with blue eyes, beautiful teeth, fine skin and complexion. Even now she can enter the lists against a great many of her younger colleagues and is one of the few beauties of the Empire who still challenge competition.

Renée Richard

Opéra

The finest contralto singer at present on the stage, and a most splendid creature. Her age is about thirty-two, and she is tall, dark and luscious, with pouting lips, teeth like ivory, marble bubbies and black hair that hangs down to her splendid buttocks. Her legs and thighs are the best in Paris, and when she appeared the other day in the part of a page, she drew all the randy rakes to her villa in the Rue Saigon to obtain a private view of her calves and the rest. She keeps herself very select, and her principal lover is a rich and jealous old swell. A gentleman, who is at the head of a large commercial firm in the provinces, paid his addresses to Mademoiselle Richard and she accepted his attentions, but, as usual, the course of true love did not run smoothly very long. They quarrelled, and for some time she heard nothing of her Adonis, and had almost forgotten him. One evening, as she was going on the stage, he appeared before her. Fortunately, she was accompanied by two gentlemen and the stage manager. She simply returned the salutation of her rejected lover and walked on. He made his way up into her dressing-room, and finding it tenanted by a young lady, one of her friends, took her by the throat and would have strangled her had not the noise of the struggle attracted attention. While the swooning girl was being attended to her assailant made his escape, and nothing has been seen of him since.

～ *Fanny Robert* ～
48 RUE DE PONTHIEU

A charming, baby face with lovely eyes, pretty little nose, teeth like a terrier's, and chestnut locks not disfigured by hair dye. Her charms are in symmetrical proportion but her breasts and buttocks are soft, as Fanny, now about twenty-eight, has been for some years the toy of the general public. Daughter of a baker of Marseilles, she drifted into a licensed brothel of that town, till she was rescued and brought to Paris by a rich lecher. Here her talents were quickly appreciated, as she gathered round her a troupe of young men under age, who, having no money, gave her bills, and by threatening their families, she filled her capacious stocking. Then she was bitten by the stage mania, and came out at the Bouffes. It was her lucky fate to be remarked by the silly Prince of Orange, since dead, after an orgy with her, and he trotted her about and made her fashionable. She acquired wealth with him, has built a villa at Cannes, and has fretted her hour upon the stage of several Parisian theatres. In spite of her money and diamonds, she is only a very silly woman with an undercurrent of whore's craftiness that has enabled her to put by plenty of pelf. She possesses every vice in the harlot's catalogue, being an inveterate sucker of women's seed and a facile Ganymede for rich sodomites. She is a frequent visitor to the sumptuous bagnio situated in Rue Chabauais, and she once fell madly in love with the stinking, sweaty negress, who is always retained on the establishment for those who like to take their game when it is 'high'. Fanny is now 'mashed' on a low pornographical journalist, but she will soon be back again to obey the orders of all who can afford to pay very highly to play with her softened globes or recline on her flabby belly.

Marie Robert

21 RUE BEAUJON

A staunch friend of Betsy Monthozon (see page 139), and the two prostitutes live in the same house. Marie is short and rather thin, with a round face, high cheek-bones, large eyes, capacious, flat mouth, filled with good teeth, dyed hair and very little of it. Her parents were *concierges*, and she received no education, teaching herself to read from the study of the lodgers' correspondence. She became a painters' model, and some budding Raphael gave her a taste of the maulstick at a very early period of her life. Her age at present is considerably over thirty, but her society is very amusing, as she is a most companionable wench, although apt to 'get the needle' very easily. She made herself conspicuous last winter by a quarrel with her namesake Fanny (see above), whom she pummelled to a jelly, and the newspapers chronicling the Homeric contest, established her reputation among the Parisian pleasure seekers, who follow in each other's fornicating footsteps like lambs to the slaughterhouse.

Reine Romani

17 RUE TRONCHET

This moll is a living enigma, as she is at the same time the most fashionable whore and the ugliest woman at present pushing her way in Paris. She is about thirty-three, tall, with a round, blotchy nose, big mouth and only tolerable teeth. Her hair is dyed and her eyes are blue, but she looks like an Irish apple woman. Happily her figure is good, her bust firm and rich, and she dresses in marvellous taste. The most aristocratic ladies condescend to copy her *toilettes*, and at every change of season refuse to order any novelties till they find out what Reine Romani is wearing. Marseilles is her birthplace, and she is renowned for the charm of her conversation, being gifted with a greater share of wit and common sense than generally falls to the lot of a woman. She strips for nobody without a preliminary introduction, and the best men in Paris are among her customers. She saves money, and refuses to stir from her coquettishly furnished little apartment on the fifth floor, where tall friends are always knocking their heads against the ceiling.

Desirée Rookmaker

60 RUE MIROMESNIL

A skinny whore of no importance, but who has by dint of impudence managed to struggle into the front rank. She is a flat-backed, long-waisted, fair cow; not too tall, and with a pointed nose, tightly drawn lips, flat teeth, Chinese eyes and no eyebrows. Garnish with a strong lisp, stuff with wadding to imitate bubbies, and serve up for the amusement of drunken Americans and benighted foreigners, who, when in her arms, fancy they have got hold of a tip-top *cocotte*. This common rag does not speak any language but French, but she makes herself understood by the strangers who visit Paris. She has never got a farthing of her own, and dresses in masculine style, out of economy.

The Sisters Roussel

11 RUE DE NAPLES

Louise, aged thirty, and Augusta, about twenty-six, are two sisters, living in the same house with their mother, who quietly fattens on the proceeds of their fornication. Their real name is Sainte-Colombe, and they come from a French colony beyond the seas, having arrived in Paris when quite young, at the death of their father. Louise and Augusta are both well educated; the elder, who is tall, stout, fair, and lascivious, being an accomplished pianist. The younger is short, dark and slighter than her sister; very fond of the game of love, she is nevertheless rather sentimental and melancholic, and is only a passive instrument in the arms of her lover, while Louise never refuses to do anything she is asked, and condescends to proffer her lips if the gentleman who pays her requires to be amused by lingering kisses instead of genuine grinding. They have both felt the pangs of maternity: Louise has two children, and Augusta one. The three little brats are wise children indeed, as they know their fathers. These two ladies may be confidently recommended, as they carry on their business in demure and old-fashioned style.

Francine de Sancey

76 AVENUE DE VILLIERS

A very ordinary-looking priestess of the Cyprian deity, with a large connection, who makes up in gaiety what she lacks in beauty. She has been the pet of the public for many years, and at present is a little off-colour, and seeks the society of youngish libertines, who are not yet able to distinguish between real and artificial beauty. Francine is a masculine woman, about thirty years of age, with sharp, well-defined features; good teeth; a slight moustache; fair hair, of which there is very little left, and a hearty laugh, which she turns on spasmodically whenever required. Her centre of love is easy of access, although she is extremely dry, and flies to the accommodating use of sweet-smelling unguents to trick the men whose rasping approach she can thus endure, while the ignorant fellows take the mixture of grease and perspiration for the viscous essence of real voluptuousness. What she really enjoys is an attack on the genital organs of one of her own sex, and, thanks to the tribadic taste of most of her fellow-workers, she is hardly ever without an attendant Sappho. Her ceaseless gossip is not devoid of wit, and she is very malicious and indiscreet, ruthlessly unveiling the secrets which she gleans while worshipping Venus according to the lesbian ritual. At whores' parties, which are given through the winter, Francine is always invited, and she keeps the table in a roar, sometimes getting under it and treating all the company, both male and female, to a warm and velvety kiss.

Ariel Sauvage

11 Rue d'Offémont

A great sleepy-eyed cow, with no accomplishments and no conversation. Her body is perfect, and her skin is as smooth as satin and as cold as marble, and it is to this physical enchantment that she owes her present position and the name she assumes. Her real denomination is that of Marguerite Biron, and she has traded on her flesh, which is as white as well-cooked veal, for many years in Paris. Russia has also received her visit, but her fornicative appeals met with no response in that cold clime, and she returned here poorer than when she left. She was always an ardent devotee of secret sports – *donna con donna* – and used to perambulate the nocturnal haunts in a low-necked dress, exposing nearly the whole of her monster hemispheres, to gather luscious food for her greedy lesbian appetite. For a short period she exhibited upon the stage her solid thighs and her massive stupidity; and she was well known to the members of our clubs for always asking to be rewarded beforehand, and never unlacing her stays till she had been paid. Her greediness drove many men away without trying to touch her, and this terrific lump of lustful flesh, with her forest of dyed hair, may esteem herself very lucky to be, at the mature age of thirty, beneath the protection of the rich silk merchant who is infatuated with the vast mistress he now possesses.

Alice Scheresne

Rue des Bassins

To see her pass, languidly sprawled out in a victoria, with a disdainful look upon her face, as if everybody stunk except her, one would take her for some high-born dame. But she is only the daughter of a gardener, and was born in Berlin about a quarter of a century since. When in her teens she was engaged by the Countess de L— to come to Paris and talk German to the children, for fifteen pounds a year, but she soon got tired of the nursery, and found a protector, who set her up and enabled her to ask a big price of any man who coveted the honour of being admitted to penetrate the tight folds of her Prussian chink. She is a tall, fair girl, with fine blue eyes, but she is as thin as a lath, and her dress is one mass of padding. Among the artists she is greatly esteemed, and sits to them for the head only, as her frame is too bony to be portrayed on canvas. When she meets with a Frenchman who professes hatred for the Germans, she puts on an English accent, and pretends to be a native of the British Isles. Those who like a bag of bones for their money, will have no reason to complain when they feel Alice's elbow sticking into their stomachs, and when they have shot the arrows that their quiver contains, they can amuse themselves by counting her ribs, which are plainly visible to the naked eye.

Marguerite Serneuil

7 RUE ROY

A brazen strumpet of thirty-five, with dyed hair, a little, aquiline nose and a pursed-up mouth. She thinks a lot of herself, and her battered body, for no earthly reason whatever. Marguerite has seen a deal of service, and will satisfy lovers of rank whores. She is always smothered in paint and saturated with scent, so that you can smell her a mile off.

Camille Sidney

26 RUE DE ROME

Whilom a star of the ballet in New York, this sober American woman of pleasure has established herself firmly, during the six years that she has been the property of the town of Paris. Her figure is slight, but she carries her twenty-six years brightly and well. Camille is pale and dark, with classically cut features, nice teeth and melting black eyes. Her pecuniary wants are principally attended to by a gentleman from Rouen, who is very faithful to his transatlantic beauty, although she seldom refuses an encounter, whenever she can slip away on the sly, or when her lord is attending to his interests in the country. Like most of her countrywomen, she will never say 'no' to anything – propose what you will.

~ *Fanny Signoret* ~

26 RUE GALILÉE

This is one of the first-class dolly-mops of our town. She sets the fashions, and the journalists, in return for an occasional rack-off, chronicle her movements in their scandalous jottings. Her mother was a whore, who late in life was taken into comfortable keeping. Fanny had just finished her education at a grand aristocratic convent, and she had no sooner returned home than her mother's paramour was into her like a shot, and all that the tribadic practices of the Lady Superior had left of her virginal membrane was destroyed immediately. Her precocious *amour* was soon discovered, and her disgusted mamma kicked her out of the house, to swell the crowd of Parisian prostitutes. She served her apprenticeship in the provinces, and coming to Paris four or five years ago, was at first under the protection of a gentleman in favour of whose Oriental proclivities she got rid of her second maidenhead. She ran up a bill at Doucet's, the man-milliner who dresses most of the venal goddesses, and worked off the score by sleeping with his son, greatly to the old tradesman's disgust. Now she is fairly at the top of the tree, and has taken to hinting that she is related to a noble English family, but that is all humbug. She is a tall, aristocratic, dark lady, with a well-cut profile, albeit her nose is perhaps a little too beaky to please some people, and her slight, well-covered frame is always tastefully and elegantly draped. Her eyes are apt to blink a little in a strong light or when she gets excited; but no one would take her to be what she is – a common whore. Her early training should have enabled her to converse with the enlightened men by whom she is surrounded, but she is very dull and quiet, and her conversation is most commonplace. She passes for a lady, evidently because she knows how to hold her tongue in the daytime, however much she may use it at night.

~ *Silly* ~
41 RUE LAFAYEFFE

The younger of two Creole sisters, who have been on the stage for the last sixteen years. The elder was known as Delval, and she possessed a most magnificent figure. In the year 1867, she appeared as a savage queen at the Porte Saint Martin Théâtre, and wore very little else but a magnificent girdle of imitation stones, the flap of which, in Egyptian style, hung down between her lovely thighs, and hid her juicy commodity. The Empress borrowed the girdle to have one made like it in real gold and jewels, and history remains mute as to whether it was used as a *ceinture de chasteté* or not. Delval took the fancy of a Russian prince who made her fortune. She has since married, and so retires from our pages. But her full-blown sister, with her large black eyes, dark skin and jellyfied bubbies, still goes on, and as she has always been very economical, is now well off. She likes a drop of liquid comfort, and has just made the conquest of an Englishman, who is young enough to be her son, and the pair never forget the existence of Bacchus, even in the midst of a sacrifice to Venus.

~ *Raphaele Sizos* ~
ODÉON THÉÂTRE

Another thin actress. She is small, young and fair, with a little old-fashioned cat's face and a prominent nasal organ. She is an average actress, and an average whore. Being of a meek disposition, and with a strong stomach, she is much used by lazy, worn-out libertines, who sometimes set her impossible tasks.

∼ *Soubise* ∼
4 Rue Appert

The oldest whore in this book, and we fully believe that there is not such an aged bitch to be found on active service anywhere. She is a tall, dark woman, with bold features; black hair; loose, dark-brown, wrinkled skin, and a tremendous mouth, full of coffee-beans. From this terrible, gaping chasm issues a charnel-house smell, and Soubise is always holding a scented handkerchief to her lips, which she still has the audacity to paint. The carmine pomade with which she rubs her pendulous labial adornments mixes with her brown saliva and runs freely down the corners on to her chin. Incredible as it may seem, this dried-up old cow still gets an occasional banknote from some idiotic lecher, and immediately bestows it on some 'ponce' with a strong stomach. She has a number of such men hanging about her, and they try to satisfy her autumnal longings for the sake of a dinner. She possesses a villa at Nice, and the broken-down, Italian swell-mobsmen find an hospitable haven of rest in her nauseous couch. In her time, she is said to have been a beautiful creature, and kings, lords and dukes have been proud to sleep with her. This is doubtless true, as even now, in spite of her love of roulette and card-playing, she is very rich indeed.

∼ *Stairs* ∼
22 Rue d'Edimbourg

A skinny actress of the Vaudeville Théâtre, whose photograph, greatly flattered, is all over Paris. She is very tall, with large dark eyes, brown hair, a pointed nose and large hands. Her talents are small, and she has nothing to recommend her, except that she is a clean whore who works her bottom up and down at a very cheap rate.

Gertrude Stevens

28 BOULEVARD DES ITALIENS

The nasal twang of this diminutive, skinny, little, consumptive, fair cow proclaims her to be a genuine importation from the United States. She is a divorced woman from New York, whence she arrived some six or seven years ago, with her two children and her banjo, after having been fired at by her husband. The gentleman who now shelters Alice Marot (see page 126) beneath his wing, took her to live with him, but got rid of her about three years ago, and she has since gone downhill steadily. She is as deaf as a post, but will not own to it, and answers her lovers anyhow by guess, making the most painfully ludicrous mistakes in consequence. Add to this that she drinks like a fish, and adores licking the salt slits of her sister whores, paying them liberally for the questionable privilege. She is noted for being one of the most clever women known for the expert consummation of oral pollution, and most of the American ladies can run Frenchwomen very hard at this enervating diversion. Gertrude's fancy-man is her coachman. In order to prevent him straying, she married him to her chambermaid, who was one of her favourite tribades, and she continues to enjoy the most extraordinary treble groups that were ever invented. She delights in the daytime to shut doors and windows, draw the curtains, light up a quantity of candles, and stripping naked, get blind drunk, while she slobbers over a woman and is herself licked, sucked and petted into oblivion.

Aimée Tessandier

125 BOULEVARD SAINT GERMAIN

She was born in 1851, and is a popular actress at the Odéon Théâtre. She is tall and thin, as black as night, with raven jet eyes and hair, and a splendid pair of carnation pulpy lips. She is well kept, but being of a very libidinous nature, is glad to change her daily bill of fare occasionally, and extract the marrow of a fresh morsel. Her temper is rather quick and lively, but as she is well educated, and very desirous of pleasing her man, a night with her may be comfortably spent by those who run after hot, dark beauties.

~ *Paule Tétat* ~

78 Rue Miromesnil

A most agreeable, fair creature, although she has no figure to speak of. But her saucy little face, with its sharp nose, small piercing eyes and good mouth and teeth, is most captivating, and her manner is exceedingly sprightly. Her keeper, a rich Greek sodomite, has just lost his fortune on the Bourse, and Paule is all alone, with a cancer in her fundament. She comes from Marseilles, and her sunny nature has enabled her to bear the blow with great fortitude. Her laughing disposition causes her to be frequently invited to the dinner parties of the *demi-mondaines*, where she keeps the fun a-going till daylight does appear. Although close upon thirty, she does not look more than twenty-five, and is celebrated for her strenuous endeavours to please the male in bed, where her agile tongue and fingers will turn a washed-out Lovelace into a second Hercules for a mere trifle.

~ *Louise Théo* ~

5 Place du Théâtre Français

Everybody knows this plump, handsome little mass of dimples, either from hearing her cackle and sing opera in Paris, London, Belgium or America, or from seeing her arch smile depicted in a photograph. She has earned a reputation for chastity, which we simply laugh at and demolish at once, but she keeps her intrigues well under control, and only surrenders her citadel after due consideration and in exchange for heavy gifts. She was born in 1852, and is the daughter of the lady who used to keep the open air *café concert*, the Pavillion de l'Horloge, in the Champs Elysées. Her mother was greatly averse to her going on the stage, and in order to be able to do as she liked she married a tailor, Théophile Vacher, and the first syllable of his Christian name forms her professional *nom de guerre*. She was then a boot-closer, and used to earn a couple of francs daily, which she duly brought home to her thick-headed master, who would be industriously stitching away as he sat, cross-legged and bootless, with his stockings, which were seldom changed, giving out a nauseous flavour that blended harmoniously with the odour of his smoking 'goose' and the decayed crutch-linings he had taken in to repair. His wife, sick of this unromantic and monotonous existence, formed the acquaintance of some of the music-hall trollops who had known her from childhood, and persuaded by them, she took no rest till she appeared at the Eldorado concert. The success of her childish untutored bearing and the tinkling of her slight voice was so great that she was quickly snapped up by a threatrical manager and has since become a queen of *opéra-bouffe*. Her voice, which was never much, has entirely left her, and she has undergone various operations to the tonsils that make her only endurable for audiences out of Paris. In her native town, in spite of her pretty ways, the saucy cock of her nose and the artful kick of her neat leg and shoe, flourishing her frills and furbelows over the senile slobberers of the stalls, she has often been hissed – poor thing! – and now does not draw a franc to the treasury. Her bosom is admirably formed, and her neck and shoulders are like those of a baby. Her eyes are black and voluptuous, and her expressive mouth is truly delicious. Madame Vacher has several children, of whom she is proudly and dotingly fond. Her discretion in love-matters is due to the fact that she is entirely bald. She has no hair on her body or head, and her particular part looks as if it had been treated like that of Oriental beauties. Her slight eyebrows are always plentifully darkened, to hide the absence of capillary adornments. She always wears a blonde wig, fixed tightly to her handsomely-shaped head, and her defect has not prevented this electrical kitten from earning a small fortune. Until she became famous at the Eldorado, she used to wear a pretty white cap, fitting close to her head, and photographs of the sweet girl thus adorned have been fished out by jealous rivals in the stage-world. Théophile, the tailor, is totally blind to his wife's *amours*, and believes that the pearls, rubies and diamonds she possesses have been presented to her by the *dilettanti*, who admire the songstress and not the woman. As if a Frenchman ever gave an actress a present without the hope of being able to enjoy her body in some way or the other!

Thérèsa

ASNIÈRES

Her real name is Emma Valadon, and her youth was passed on a charlatan's cart, travelling from fair to fair to tear out teeth and cure all human ills. The gentleman in the red wig, whose high and mighty function was to grind an organ while the Dulcamara was breaking the jaws of the village louts in order to drown their cries of agony, seduced the girl, who was very ugly. She has never been handsome, having a heavy jowl, an ugly figure and nothing to relieve her vulgarity but a lovely pair of hands, small, white and delicate, like those of a duchess. She is dark, with bold eyes and a tremendous mouth, which she uses like Sappho, and glories in the sport, with difficulty ungluing her lips from the *pubis* of the victim who has taken her fancy. Strange to say, this rough and vulgar cow is a born musician, and her voice is most charming, while no one can give better effect to a song of the sentimental or patriotic order. Some sixteen years ago, Thérèsa's name first got famous at the music-halls, and she was sent for to the Tuileries, where the Empress and her maids of honour would join in the choruses of her most suggestive ditties. Since then she has been quite as successful on the real stage, and is the idol of the Parisian populace. She is now forty-six years old, and has just got married to a handsome butcher lad, whose manly beauty has captivated her, as her money-bags have captivated him. The curse of her life has been her gluttonous rage for active tribadism, but her husband is very jealous of this mania, and beats her till she is black and blue whenever he catches his wife with her head between the thighs of one of her lady friends. She possesses a magnificent house and grounds at Asnières, the favourite riverside haunt of the counter-jumper and his troll, and is very kind and hospitable. Her mother is a *concierge*, Passage des Deux Sœurs, and is an expert fortune-teller. Thérèsa is occasionally sought after by rich strangers, who spend a few hours with her out of curiosity. If the rakes who seek the enjoyment of her body bring a fresh-looking girl with them, as a sacrifice to the insatiable Sappho, they will not be asked for any fee, but the victim, if she responds to Thérèsa's kisses with becoming lust and unequivocal, gushing signs of pleasure, will be presented with a bracelet, or some such grateful and costly present. Her memoirs were published in 1865, but the book is a made-up pack of lies.

Rachel Therka

48 BOULEVARD HAUSSMANN

A spare, meagre whore, about twenty-seven. She is fair, with dark eyes and good teeth, a pointed proboscis and a half-starved look, which she does not belie, as the tiny aperture between her scraggy thighs is as cold as a dog's nose, and always very dry, besides being but scantily covered with hair. She calls herself an Austrian, and speaks German better than French, but she may hail from Prussia or Hungary for aught we know. Two younger sisters, who are not *à la mode*, like Rachel, and having a child a-piece, to say nothing of the mother of the lot, all live huddled together, in one small apartment, and the produce of Rachel's lean charms goes to pay the butcher and baker. Therka is cunning, and she hangs on to richer whores. She invites them to dinner and they are obliged to return the compliment. In their villas, she occasionally wheedles herself into the embrace of some rich rake whom she would never otherwise have met, but the deluded wretches seldom, if ever, come twice to drink at Rachel's fountain. She gives out that an old married lecher pays her liberally and keeps in the background, but as the elderly party is never seen, we may suppose that his existence is entirely mythical, and that Rachel keeps herself afloat by the precarious presents of occasional combats, which like the hairs on her centre of enjoyment are few and far between.

The Sisters Thibaut

FOLIES-DRAMATIQUES THÉÂTRE

M. Thibaut, an ex-regimental bandmaster, was killed in the Champs Elysées by a stray obus, during the insurrection of the Commune in April 1871, and he left his wife and three daughters, Berthe, Blanche and Jeanne, to mourn his loss. Their inheritance consisted in a legacy of debt and poverty, so Berthe, the eldest, came out at the Opéra Comique, Blanche made her *début* at the Opéra, and Jeanne, who is now only eighteen, stopped at home and darned their stockings. Berthe and Blanche are of a good stature – fair, with plump thick bodies and bold handsome features. They are very much alike in appearance, but Berthe is lively and Blanche inclined to sadness. Their united age is very little over sixty. The father's debts had to be paid, so Berthe left the stage and took a lover, and she has never returned to the boards. Blanche had also to sell herself, and she has become an actress of *opéra-bouffe*. Both are genial, kind whores, and they adore their little sister, who has not yet lost her rose.

～ *Renée Thierry* ～

GYMNASE THÉÂTRE

This is the young beginner to whom we briefly alluded on page 62, by the name of 'Netty', but she has now taken the above title. The terrible whore who gave her birth had her brought up for the operatic stage, but she has gone in for light comedy and heavy fornication. She is certainly not more than eighteen and is therefore deserving of adoration, as there are very few really young whores in Paris. She is small and dark, with a Roman nose, a nice little mouth and teeth and a symmetrical figure, as yet not quite developed. Her mother sells her at a figure that places her within the reach of moderately rich libertines, and the unripe beauty responds quickly to the magnetic touch of the staff of life, and cheerfully essays the voluptuous byplay, at which she is at present deliciously awkward.

∾ *Marie Thorcy* ∾
15 RUE PORTALIS

A dark little actress, with a neat, well-rounded figure, chubby face, blue-black hair and large, melting, inquisitive eyes to match. Her mouth, with its ruby, rich, pouting lips and white projecting teeth, is a luscious invitation to forbidden joys, and she is well worthy of notice, as she has not been too much sullied. Her age is about twenty-two, and when she came out at the Palais Royal Théâtre, some four years ago, she was quickly secured by a Jewish banker of Belgian extraction, with whom she has lived ever since. Her real name is Theuriet, and she is tolerably intelligent, a good *pianiste*, and very fond of her comfortable little home. She is none the less accessible to young men, but she dislikes old rakes, and will be found shy and coy in bed, although greatly enjoying the attack of a robust suitor.

∾ *Jeanne de Trémont* ∾
72 BOULEVARD MALESHERBES

A thin bitch, very ugly as to her face, which is the worst part about her, but as her bones are sufficiently covered, she will be esteemed a delicate morsel by amateurs who do not delight in a super-abundance of flesh. She has got curious little Chinese eyes, and is known as 'Louchon', in consequence. She adores horse exercise, and likes to find a hearty fellow waiting for her when she gets off her steed with her *clitoris* excited by the rubbing of the saddle. As her temper is good and her manner cordial, she is never in want of customers, and her sister whores are very pleased to go about with her, as she does not try to captivate and steal away the hearts of their lovers. She paints her face an inch thick, but the enamel rubs off in bed, and as her friends adore her other charms, no one tells her to abjure cosmetics. She will generally be found in the company of Laure Decroze and Clara Dermigny (see pages 46 and 52).

～ *Marguerite Ugalde* ～
RUE PERGOLÈSE

Her mother was a celebrated singer of comic opera, and a well-known woman of pleasure. Her daughter has only been singing in *opéra-bouffe* for about two years, and she has already had many admirers fluttering round her. She was supposed to be a virgin, a long time after her maidenhead had ceased to be intact, but having been so played with and lasciviously caressed she was only physically a maid, while yet in her teens. Marguerite is about twenty-one, of average stature, with a strong, well-made frame, a bold face, laughing blue eyes and a large, voluptuous mouth. She is as yet very girlish, and her pretty, childish blandishments are very refreshing to the jaded senses. For preliminary play, and a long, sensual romp, when she will give and take indecent slaps and lascivious pinches, this budding charmer stands unrivalled in the Parisian market of white slaves.

～ *Lucy Vailly* ～
71 RUE NEUVE FORTIN

She is tall, thin and well built, of fair complexion, but just a little used-up and washed-out, as she is about thirty, and has been a prostitute ever since she was quite a young girl. Her bubbies are scanty, but her legs are good, and she is fond of undressing when in society, and exhibiting all her charms freely and shamelessly. She is very miserly, even to blowing out all the candles in her bedroom till only one is left, but she does not seem to be very rich, notwithstanding her economy. She is tormented by the fear of approaching obesity, and does all she can in the way of exercise so as not to get fat. As night comes on, she is indefatigable, and leaves no stone unturned, so as not to go home alone. In bed, she is as lithe as a serpent, and as accommodating as the most exacting lover can desire. Lucy has tried Sapphism, but does not like it, and prefers humouring the caprices of the men, for very modest gratuities.

Louise Valtesse

98 Boulevard Malesherbes

She calls herself Valtesse 'de la Bigne', which is the name of a man she once lived with, so she has adopted it for her own. He is now paralysed, but still visits her. At the time we write, she is suspiciously near forty, but she is a most lovely, fair woman, with a quantity of auburn hair, that is all genuine, both in length and colour. Her eyes are blue, the nose rather large, and her features are not well-chiselled. Her body is far from perfect; she possesses no bosom to speak of; her waist is thick and ungainly, and her belly is very flat indeed. But she is never tired, and as the charm of joy is bountifully shaded with moss of true Venetian red, and always ready, full of burning foam, we must ascribe her continued success to this gift of nature. Her skin is as fair as an English country girl's, and she uses no perfumes of any kind; nothing but a little rice powder. At the age of fifteen, she was a stockingless, bootless, painter's model, and then lived for some years in Belgium with a dramatic author. Returning to Paris, she passed a life of misery with a reporter for the press, till a Turkish banker built the foundation of the enormous fortune she now possesses, and returning to her first lover, she earned the nickname of the 'Painter's Union'. A celebrated young artist, whose military studies are as well known in England as in France, has kept her for ten years, and dwells opposite her house. All his gains go to her, but she sleeps with another wielder of the brush, his intimate friend, but only in secret. All the famous artists of the day passed into her bed in turns, and she refused them nothing, not even when they turned her round and sacrificed to Venus on the Jesuitical altar. Ever since her most tender youth, her brother has been her lover, and he still visits her, living on her earnings and sleeping in her arms when she is disengaged. This incestuous intercourse is one of the greatest delights of her life, varied with furious lesbianism, when-ever occasion offers. Her house is a marvel of rich and tasteful decoration, recalling several epochs. Her pictures, pottery and furniture are priceless, and she reposes in a solid gilt bronze bedstead, representing a fantastically shaped boat, the description of which will be found in Zola's novel, *Nana*. She has a young sister who ran away with one of her elderly subscribers, and a daughter who is at school. This courtesan, who resembles the heroine of de Sade's bloody tale, *Juliette*, is well educated and has written a romance, called *Isola*. It is whispered that she intends to publish her collection of love letters, and, if she does so, amateurs of scandal will have a rich and rare treat. Her notepaper bears the cynical motto, 'Ego', so visitors to her shrine must be prepared to pay dearly for the short hour she allows them, during which they may enjoy any part of her body they like, without the least restriction being placed upon the most horrible leches, however dirty and degrading. The ambitious bitch has also meddled in politics, and she was a friend of the late statesman, Gambetta, in whom she instilled the ideas that led to the war in Tonkin. Her palace is well worthy of a visit, and she owns a delightful *bijou* residence at Ville d'Avray, 12 Avenue de la Grille. Louise is very mean, but there is method in her meanness. She does not grudge giving a high price for an artistic object that will adorn her rooms, as she has very good taste; but she murmurs at the expense of a dinner or a party; keeps no horses or carriages, and rides on the democratic tramway to save a cab-fare. She is not such a fool as to buy expensive *toilettes*, and in winter often economises a pair of gloves by hiding her naked hands in her muff. When an artist calls to see her, she has a piece of vellum ready cut in fan-shape, and pushing a colour-box into his hand, she breathes down his neck while he dashes off a design, which she makes him sign with his name in full. She gets autographs of famous men in the same way; to say nothing of copies of rare books with dedications and little sketches and pictures. She evidently means to have a great sale by public auction one of these days. All men are equal, when stripped to the skin, says Valtesse, and she makes no difference between a prince and a peasant, except that one has got money and the other has not. So she allows herself to be rummaged by anybody, and takes what she can get, refusing no man, and pocketing the slightest fee. Every Sunday, she is at home to an old subscriber, who gives her two napoleons, and she refuses many a junketing so as to stop and grasp the couple of gold pieces. If, when in the society of learned or distinguished persons, some subject is mentioned of which she knows nothing, she holds her tongue, and buys in secret the book that will teach her what she has hitherto ignored. So we may venture to state, without fear of contradiction, that Valtesse is one of the most handsome and clever of the whores of our time, resembling a courtesan of ancient Greece, and she is the most curious example of the prosperity of vice in our sensual city that we have been enabled to depict for the benefit of our randy readers.

Marie Van Zandt

1 Rue Lincoln

The sensation of the year, as she has appeared on the stage of the Opéra Comique and has taken the town by storm. Her age is only nineteen, and she is a native of the Dutch colonies belonging to Spain. Her childhood has been passed in North America, so that she speaks English with a Dutch accent, and French with a mixed intonation, difficult to define. She is a fair little cat, with small blue eyes and nice teeth, but her figure has not yet blossomed into shape. She is sprightly, and hysterical, but can put away comfortably three bottles of brandy a day. She is always playing off practical jokes upon her friends, and pretends to be a merry, guileless maiden; but she is very artful at bottom, and acts in obedience to the secret instructions of her vulgar old mother, who lives on her earnings. Like all young actresses just out, she is supposed to be intact; but this is not the case, as she has several careful lovers after her, who all take care not to get her with child. Marie has an elder sister, very ugly, who acts as her maid. She is very capricious, and drives her manager mad by her unpunctuality and careless conduct at rehearsal.

Noémie Vernon

41 Rue de Lisbonne

A star of *opéra-bouffe*, and a very devoted worshipper of Priapus. She is a little, old-fashioned woman, of about twenty-five years of age, with black eyes and hair, agreeable face and fine breasts; but her thighs and legs are far from being properly covered with flesh. She is a good creature, and her scale of charges places her clean body within the reach of all.

Clémence Vilain

23 RUE CAUMARTIN

One of the finest women of her day, when in the zenith of her beauty, but now she is about forty, and having feathered her nest to a pretty tune, lives soberly and comfortably in her well-appointed little apartment, enlivened by the visits of ancient lovers, and receiving the discreet attentions of one or two rich and faithful old boys. Her name, 'Vilain', is synonymous with 'ugliness' and was bestowed upon her in graceful irony when she was a young woman. She is tall and thin, with a prominent nose and a crooked, merry mouth, and she is very jolly and hospitable, having no cares of any kind. In short, a clean, elderly piece, with not an atom of vice about her.

Constance Viola

43 RUE DES BELLES-FEUILLES

Although very little over forty, this splendid, fair, healthy-skinned whore, with a face like a full moon and a tantalising hair wart on her cheek, is very little known to the present generation. She was one of the best whores of the Third Empire, and having saved up money, has retired with her mother to the above comfortable suburban residence. A few old generals and ex-chamberlains of Napoleon the Third occasionally go round and see her, and she shakes a noble but withered *scrotum*, and talks of the old glories of the Tuileries, drawing a tear from the bleary eye of the corrupt old courtier, and a few drops of colourless fluid from his exhausted canal. Constance would be gratefully flattered by the visit of a younger man, and would gladly place her lumps of melting flesh at his disposal.

Valentine Volsy
GYMNASE THÉÂTRE

A plump, fair beauty, on the shady side of thirty, with a round face and good eyes, teeth and complexion. She is of a very retiring disposition, and is principally protected by an old gentleman. Her charms are in good order, as she does not knock about much, but her talents as an actress are only second-rate. She dresses in excellent taste, and is one of the few actress-whores that a man can take out with him without feeling disgraced, as she looks like a real lady, and 'behaves as such'.

Eliane Volter
47 RUE GALILÉE

A lovely, dark woman, of about thirty-eight years of age, with a commanding presence, and a nice figure, while her charms are all within proper bounds. She was formerly a ballet-girl at the Paris Opéra, and migrated to Russia, where she was the pet of St Petersburg for many years. Sometimes she takes the name of 'Ivanowitch', and pretends to be a Russian lady. She has a big girl, about fourteen years of age, and mamma works very hard to keep her in clothing of fashionable cut and pay her school bill. Eliane likes youths, and has a rare connection among embryo rakes, with their beards just sprouting.

Marguerite Vrignault
91 RUE DE BALZAC

Up to within the last year, this young whore was acting at the Gymnase, whither she had gone on leaving the Conservatoire. She earned no histrionic laurels, so has given up the stage entirely, and contents herself with the free life of a demirep. What is bred in the bone, etc., is exemplified here, as Marguerite is the daughter of a rank old whore, who has now retired from active warfare. Vrignault is now about twenty-two; not too tall; slight figure, with small, hard, nicely formed breasts; a 'prunes and prism' sort of mouth; eyes half-closed, and a very prudish demeanour. An elderly lover keeps the financial ball a-rolling, and she has a little boy by him. She has a younger sister, Marthe, who has just come out at the Vaudeville. If she follows the advice of Marguerite, who is well educated and very artful, she will be sure to thrive. Our charmer has lowered her tariff lately, on account of the damage done to her pretty face by a carriage accident, which marked her with an ugly scar under her left eye.

Adèle de Wagnère
6 Rue Delaborde

A creamy, nut-brown bitch, about twenty-eight years of age, with hazel eyes, large open nostrils, a luscious, capacious mouth, which is frequently prostituted, and a fine, healthy figure, with bold, soft bubbies. The growth of hair on her private cavity is truly admirable in its wild tangle, and the same tufts of raven blackness luxuriate abundantly beneath her sturdy arms. She is kept by a businessman, who, hard at work all day, only turns up at night, and believes in the fidelity of his mistress. She, however, drives a brisk afternoon trade, and on a rainy day, when your time and your testicles hang heavy on your hands, you cannot do better than call upon Adèle, and surrender to the mercenary but clever caresses of this blowsy enchantress.

Louise Williams
28 Rue Tronchet

A French woman; fair and pale; her beauty faded by reason of the ardour of her lesbian passions. There never was a madder tribade, or a more thorough-paced whore. She is now about twenty-nine, and has perambulated Paris at night, from music-halls to theatres and from balls to supper-rooms, for the last eight years. When men's bounties fail her, she begs of the women, who like her caresses, and in return for her active Sapphic tricks, reward her liberally. She has thoroughly exhausted the catalogue of human folly, and no lech surprises her, nor will she refuse any man, however monstrous his longings may be. Her large, hysterical, blue orbs prove the intensity of her depraved temperament, and she is generally known as 'Loulou'.

Emilie Williams

60 Rue Miromesnil

An ugly, old sow, whose age we refrain from guessing at. She is of chestnut hue; short; with large, watery, brown eyes; and such a horrible nose and mouth that she is known as 'The Seal'. This fleshy matron does a fair trade, so we suppose there must be more amateurs than we dream of in our philosophy for such stinking whores, who are the perfection of painted, sepulchral ugliness. Her backside and bubbies shake as she walks, like a badly-made *blanc-mange*, and she is always escorted by five or six dogs, as wheezy as their mistress, and full of fleas.

Linda Zambrowska

2 Rue des Colonnes

A pale, fair and silly whore, of Polish extraction but with a dash of Spanish blood in her veins. She is about twenty-eight, and has attained a little notoriety this year by being seen in the company of her richer sister in the trade, Fanny Robert. She is an inveterate gambler, and was in pawn this summer at Luchon, having lost her little all at baccarat. She circularised all her Parisian friends, and managed to struggle home. She can be seen, and her stout body enjoyed, for the small sum of twenty francs, and she gives visitors full value for money. Linda is very respectable, healthy, kind and well educated and now awaits a Messiah, in the person of a generous keeper.

Licensed Brothels of Paris

Paris is divided into twenty arrondissements

116	Rue d'Aboukir	II
131	Rue d'Aboukir	II
8	Rue d'Amboise	II
10	Rue d'Amboise	II
37B	Rue Sainte-Anne	I
39	Rue Sainte-Anne	I
25	Rue Sainte-Appoline	II
70	Boulevard de Belleville	XX
116	Boulevard de Belleville	XX
4	Rue Blondel	III
32	Rue Blondel	II
13	Rue de la Bucherie	V
17	Passage Cardinet	XVII
12	Rue de Charbanais	
	(*see note a*)	II
106	Boulevard de la Chapelle	
		XIX
157	Rue de la Chapelle	XVIII
25	Rue de la Charbonnière	
		XVIII
18	Boulevard de Charonne	XX
30	Boulevard de Charonne	XX
164	Rue de Charonne	XX
7	Rue des Ciseaux	VI
8	Rue Colbert	II
289	Rue Saint-Denis	II
63	Bvd Edgar-Quintet	XIV
67	Bvd Edgar-Quintet	XIV
71	Bvd Edgar-Quintet	XIV
12	Rue Feydeau	II
25	Rue des Filles-Dieu	II
29	Rue des Filles-Dieu	II
1	Rue Fleury	XVIII
10	Rue de Fourcy	IV
21	Rue Sainte-Foy	II

24	Rue Sainte-Foy	II
2	Rue Fragonard	XVII
69	Rue Galande	V
15	Rue Saint-Gregoire-	
	de-Tours	VI
5	Boulevard de Grenelle	XV
83	Boulevard de Grenelle	XV
93	Boulevard de Grenelle	XV
95	Boulevard de Grenelle	XV
113	Boulevard de Grenelle	XV
115	Boulevard de Grenelle	XV
125	Boulevard de Grenelle	XV
127	Boulevard de Grenelle	XV
26	Rue Greneta	II & III
1	Rue Harvey	XIII
7	Rue Harvey	XIII
9	Rue Harvey	XIII
11	Rue Harvey	XIII
11	Rue de l'Hôtel-de-Ville	IV
19	Rue de l'Hôtel-de-Ville	IV
9	Boulevard d'Italie	XIII
11	Boulevard d'Italie	XIII
23	Bvd Saint-Jacques	XIV
47	Bvd Saint-Jacques	XIV
8	Rue des Jardins-	
	Saint-Paul	IV
15	Rue Jean-Beausire	IV
9	Rue Jean-Jacques	
	Rousseau	I
7	Rue Jolivet	XIV
4	Rue Joubert (*see note b*)	IX
24	Avenue de Lowendall	XV
42	Rue de la Lune	II
23	Rue Maitre-Albert	V
33	Rue Saint-Marc	II

30	Rue Sainte-Marguerite I	59	Rue Saint-Sauveur II
29	Rue Maubuée VI	4	Boulevard Serurier XIX
20	Rue Mauconseil I	2	Rue Steinkerque XVIII
49	Rue Mazarine (*see note c*) VI	106	Avenue de Suffren XV
88	Bvd Ménilmontant XX	56	Rue Taitbout (*see note g*) ix
1	Rue Miollis XV	11	Rue Thérèse I
14	Rue Monthyon	42	Rue de Tocqueville XVII
	(*see note d*) IX	19	Rue Traversière XII
112	Rue de Montreuil XI	19	Place du Trône XI
24	Rue des Moulins (*see note e*) I	40	Rue de la Victoire
164	Rue Oberkampf XI		(*see note h*) X
4	Rue aux Ours III	22	Bvd de la Villette XIX
7	Rue du Pélican I	28	Bvd de la Villette XIX
38	Rue Philippe-de-Girard	164	Bvd de la Villette XIX
	XVIII	214	Bvd de la Villette XIX
94	Boulevard Picpus XII	226	Bvd de la Villette XIX
8	Rue Portalès II	236	Bvd de la Villette XIX
92	Rue de Provence (*note f*) ix	1	Cours de Vincennes XX
5	Rue des Quatre-Vents VI	54	Cours de Vincennes XX

Licensed Brothels in the Suburbs

Aubervilliers	117 Route de Flandre
Boulogne	199 Rue de la Plaine
Courbevoie	2, 3 and 5 Rue de Nanterre
Saint Denis	1 Au Barrage
	91 Route de Perrefitte
	8 Route de la Revolte
Pantin	38 Rue de Flandre
Romainville	8 Rue de la Ferme
Vincennes	33 Rue du Levant

Notes to the Licensed Brothels

(a) The finest bagnio in the world. Each room is decorated in a
different style, regardless of expense. The bathing chamber is
sumptuously arranged and may be used in company of a chosen
nymph, for the charge of 100 francs. The management issues an
illustrated book giving a view of the principal saloons. A negress is

kept on the establishment. This is a favourite resort of the upper ten, and many ladies, both in society and out of it, come here alone, or with their lovers, for lesbian diversions.

(b) A good old-fashioned bordel. The reception room upstairs is fitted with ceiling and walls of looking glass. This was once one of the most famous houses of ill-fame in Paris, when under the direction of Madame Farcy. She has since retired into the country, and has built a church, and made herself renowned by her endless charitable bounties. Her initials are still to be seen on the walls, on the backs of the ivory hair-brushes, etc.

(c) The favourite resort of the students of the Latin Quarter. On Thursday and Sunday nights, it is difficult to find a slave disengaged, and the embryo doctors and lawyers are forced to wait their turn.

(d) Another good house, rather cheaper than the first two we have mentioned, but with a fine selection of girls of all sizes and colours.

(e) A very curious old mansion, a relic of ancient times. It has recently been restored at great cost and the electric light has been installed there. Possesses a bold entrance, into which rich clients drive bodily with their carriages, thus ensuring perfect secrecy. Is much frequented during the daytime.

(f) May be recommended for its excessive cheapness, while the obliging ladies are just as expert as at the dearer houses. Entrance fee: 5 francs, and a few francs gratuity to the mistress of an hour.

(g) A comfortable little house. Very dear, but the stout hostess is kind and obliging. She is a fine woman, and will give a *rendezvous* in the town, but not at her own place.

(h) Madame Jeanne de Rieux is the mistress of this stew, which is merely a resort for those who derive pleasure from the use of a female's lips and tongue. The women are here divided into classes, namely: Professors, Second Professors, Beginners and Novices. The Professors are half-naked; the others are dressed as servants, with black costumes and aprons. Madame calls them her 'pupils', and they earn their titles by their degree of proficiency in the art of labial pollution. The fee is 10 francs per woman engaged.

∽ Index of the ∽
Pretty Women of Paris

Wordsworth Classic Erotica